CONSTABLE BY THE STREAM

as Nicholas Rhea
Constable on the Hill
Constable on the Prowl
Constable Around the Village
Constable Across the Moors
Constable in the Dale
Constable by the Sea
Constable Along the Lane
Constable Through the
  Meadow
Constable at the Double
Constable in Disguise
Constable Among the Heather
Portrait of the North York
  Moors

as Peter N. Walker
Murders and Mysteries from
  the North Yorks Moors
Folk Tales from the North
  York Moors
Murders and Mysteries from
  the Yorkshire Dales
Folk Stories from the
  Yorkshire Dales
Carnaby and the Hijackers
Carnaby and the Gaolbreakers
Carnaby and the Assassins
Carnaby and the Conspirators
Carnaby and the Saboteurs
Fatal Accident
Panda One on Duty
Special Duty
Carnaby and the Eliminators
Identification Parade

Carnaby and the
  Demonstrators
Panda One Investigates
Carnaby and the Infiltrators
The Dovingsby Death
Carnaby and the
  Kidnappers
The MacIntyre Plot
Missing from Home
Witchcraft for Panda One
Target Criminal
Carnaby and the
  Counterfeiters
The Carlton Plot
Siege for Panda One
Teenage Cop
Carnaby and the
  Campaigners
Robber in a Mole Trap

as Christopher Coram
A Call to Danger
A Call to Die
Death in Ptarmigan Forest
Death on the Motorway
Murder by the Lake
Murder beneath the Trees
Prisoner on the Dam
Prisoner on the Run

as Tom Ferris
Espionage for a Lady

as Andrew Arncliffe
Murder after the Holiday

Constable by the Stream

NICHOLAS RHEA

Nicholas Rhea

ROBERT HALE · LONDON

© *Nicholas Rhea 1991*
First published in Great Britain 1991

ISBN 0 7090 4607 3

Robert Hale Limited
Clerkenwell House
Clerkenwell Green
London EC1R 0HT

Photoset in Plantin in North Wales by
Derek Doyle & Associates, Mold, Clwyd.
Printed in Great Britain by
St Edmundsbury Press, Bury St Edmunds, Suffolk.
Bound by WBC Bookbinders Ltd, Bridgend, Glamorgan.

Contents

1   Nymphs of Still Waters

And she forgot the stars, the moon, the sun,
And she forgot the blue above the trees,
And she forgot the dells where waters run,
And she forgot the chilly autumn breeze.
John Keats (1795–1821)

After a beautiful and memorable early morning experience, I could add my own lines to Keats's verse; they would read,

And she forgot she had no bathing suit on.
And she forgot the masculine eye that sees.

To be strictly accurate, my lines should read 'they' instead of 'she', because my early morning patrol was enlivened and enhanced by the sight of two beautiful maidens, two sylphs, two nubile nymphs bathing in a remote lake. And both were nude.

At first I thought I was dreaming, and then I wondered whether I was experiencing one of those moments that seem to happen only to other people, like seeing fairies or ghosts or experiencing religious visions. Those who cannot see them do not believe or understand those who can.

But those enchanting figures were real enough. Not real enough to touch, of course, but real enough to watch.

I was spellbound as I saw them splashing in the clear waters and heard their laughter ringing bell-like in the powerful silence of that morning.

As I gazed upon the delights before me I was reminded of

the many legends, mainly Grecian but some British, which tell of water nymphs. Those lovely goddess-like creatures have, over the centuries, been inextricably linked with springs and streams and here was I, seeing two dream-like creatures frolicking in a quiet lake before six o'clock one brisk and bright spring morning.

I knew of ancient stories which told of such heavenly sights. Homer wrote of nymphs which were semi-divine maidens; they inhabited waters like seas, lakes, rivers and fountains and there is a verse which says,

> They spring from fountains and from sacred groves,
> And holy streams that flow into the sea.

Here in the north of England, there are similar tales. Some local, but ancient stories continue to associate holy maidens with wells and springs, one of which flows near Giggleswick in the Yorkshire Dales. This is the famous Ebbing and Flowing Well whose origins are so ancient that they have been lost in the passage of time. The creation of this magic spring is said to have occurred long before the foundation of Christianity. The story tells of a maiden who was fleeing for her life; she prayed to the gods that she would escape her pursuer.

When she reached the point where the spring now flows, the gods answered her prayers. She was instantly turned into the magic spring which continues to ebb and flow from a mysterious underground source. Its surface rises and falls in a most curious manner. Its movement is sometimes accompanied by sighs and it is said that these are sighs of relief coming from that hunted nymph.

But in my own pleasure at sighting two nudes by the lake, I realized there was a very practical explanation. These were not sprites or legendary nymphs, but two very real and very beautiful young women. Nonetheless, it must be said that the moment was magical because these were two of the most beautiful of maidens. Furthermore, the ethereal quality of the morning did add enchantment. It was a stunning opening to that day's duty and I was reminded of the wise words of a former chief constable who said, 'Men who do not appreciate the beauty of a naked woman must have something wrong with them!'

However, I had work to do which was why I was in this wood at such an early hour. From time to time, we got reports of escapees from local Borstal institutions or even mental hospitals and on occasions these young men would sleep rough in local woodlands. They'd build shelters among the undergrowth and would light fires to keep themselves warm or to provide hot meals – sometimes the rising smoke was a sign of their presence.

Other indications came with the raiding of isolated farms for food like raw turnips or potatoes, eggs or milk. Some would even break into village houses or shops in their hunt for food or cash, and some had been known to steal a change of clothing or footwear.

In recent days, I had received reports of a suspicious man in these woods and this made me wonder if we had an escapee in the vicinity, even if there had been no other evidence of his presence. From the reports, I felt sure someone was lurking there and checked my own lists of recent escapees and wanted persons. But I found none that would be of direct interest to me as the village constable of Aidensfield. I had not received any reports of stolen food or unlawful entry into premises, nor had I received any reports of gunshots or traps used by poachers in that woodland. In short, the mystery man was something of a puzzle, but in truth he was not of any pressing concern because he did not seem to be engaged upon any unlawful activity. He might be nothing more than a keen ornithologist or a local person taking an early-morning stroll – but, as the village constable, it would be useful to know what he was doing, if only to placate those who worried about him.

I decided not to make any special effort to locate him; instead, I would be aware of his presence and remain alert for further sightings or reports of wrongdoing.

On that lovely morning, therefore, I was patrolling a 'route', as we called the duty. This gave me the opportunity to have a quiet walk among the trees just to see if there was any substance to the mystery-man stories. Reports suggested he'd been lurking among the mixed coniferous and deciduous trees which adorned a hillside to the south-west of Aidensfield. The first report came from a gamekeeper; he'd seen the fellow at a distance shortly before five o'clock one morning but had lost sight of him among the trees. Quite naturally, he suspected poachers. Then, on another day, around 5.30 in the morning, a cowman had spotted the man; his version was that the character was a youngish man with long hair who seemed to be furtively clambering among the hillside shrubs and trees. He seemed to have been hurrying from the lake which lay deep in a small valley within that woodland. The cowman had been unable to pursue the fellow because he was herding his cows into the mistal for milking and lacked the necessary time to locate him. He did say, however, that the man did not appear to be doing anything suspicious and he thought he might be camping in the woods.

I had these reports in mind as I'd started that early morning route at 5 a.m. My scheduled patrol had to include the villages of Elsinby and Maddleskirk; I was to be at each of them at 6 a.m. and 7 a.m. respectively and was to end that patrol at my police house at 8 a.m.

As the stretch of woodland in question lay within that route, and as I had not yet solved the mystery of the man among the trees, I decided I would explore the area. It would add purpose to my solitary walk.

I found myself walking along a deserted cart track which skirted the lower edge of the wood and from there I turned along a smaller path which led to the bottom lake. There are three lakes in these woods; they are all fed by the same stream which rises in the hills above, the top lake overflowing to form the middle one, and the middle one overflowing into the bottom one. The bottom one is the largest of the trio and offers good fishing as well as a wealth of rare and interesting wildlife ranging from plants to birds, via trees, fish and insects. It is, in fact, noted for its dragonflies and damselflies and the entire area, which is on private property, has been designated a nature reserve.

Among the structures around the lakes is a shelter of rough timber built by some local boy scouts to house their canoes and I knew to search there for signs of a secretive presence. I found nothing. During my perambulations, I walked quietly through the trees, avoiding the paths that would give rise to unwelcome noise, avoiding fallen twigs which would crack if I stood on them or thick coverings of leaves which would rustle. If there was anyone living rough hereabouts, I did not want to give warning of my approach by sending birds chattering from me.

A startled pheasant or wood pigeon can create an awful din, while the alarm call of a blackbird is enough to alert any countryman. Thus I moved gingerly and carefully about my business, eyes and ears alert as I emulated generations of gamekeepers in my stealthy prowling. After thoroughly checking the ground around the bottom lake, I moved to the middle one and repeated my search, again with no success. And then, as I climbed through the trees to the top and smallest lake, only marginally larger than a good village pond, I heard sounds. Voices. Light voices. Movements among the undergrowth. Bushes rustling. A chaffinch flying off in noisy alarm. A twig cracking. Laughter. Water splashing ...

So there *was* somebody! I froze. I stood like a statue among the freshly leafed trees, not making a sound as I tried to gauge the precise location of those sounds. I decided they came from the north-eastern corner of the lake, close to the entry point of the stream which fed it. I knew that the forest track ran past that point too ... if there was a vehicle, it would be parked nearby. I could obtain its registration number, if necessary.

It was now that my local knowledge proved valuable because I knew of a large, chair-shaped boulder near the western shore and realized it would provide me with a secure vantage point. I could hide behind it as I watched the activities of the visitors. Moving quickly, silently and confidently through the trees, I gained the big rock and began to scan the water.

It was then that I saw two heads near the centre of the lake.

Two young women were bathing there, neither wearing a swimming cap but they were keeping their heads above the surface. One was a light blonde while the other was also blonde but of a slightly darker shade. They swam with ease, chattering to each other as they moved gracefully through the smooth water with the morning sun glinting from the surface. There was the slightest hint of a haze over the lake, a misty atmosphere which intensified towards the distant shore. But I could see no one else nor could I discern any vehicle parked nearby. I wondered if the man seen earlier had any links with these girls.

I did not recognize either of them and was about to leave when they emerged from the water. Both were exquisitely beautiful and splendidly shaped – and they were completely naked. As they rose from the cool, clear waters I watched with fascination as their long, slender limbs carried them to the distant shore; they halted near the edge, turned and scooped handfuls of clean water with which they washed their lithe young bodies. They presented a sight to be treasured, a sight to be captured for ever by a skilled artist. But there was no artist to observe them – just an appreciative village constable. The water cascaded between their shapely and ample breasts, down their flat stomachs, flowing between their legs and around their thighs as they rinsed away the water-borne particles which clung to them.

They continued with their ablutions until they had washed away every piece of surplus mud and greenery which had been carried from the lake and its floor. Unabashed, uninhibited, free and beautiful, they cleaned themselves, then suddenly turned and ran off.

I heard them laughing with joy as they vanished among the distant trees and shrubs. I waited. I did not want to announce my intrusive presence in any way, nor did I want them to think I had been spying on them. Did they visit this lake each morning? Were they camping nearby? Were they visitors? And it was so early ... I looked at my watch. 5.50. Who would rise for a swim before six in a chilly fresh-water lake? No one that I knew....

But they had vanished. I did not see them depart nor did I hear any more voices. They had vanished beyond the thick greenery at the far end of the lake and I waited for a long time, forgetting that I had to be in Elsinby at 6 a.m.! I never made that rendezvous but walked from the wood in something of a daze. I wondered if I had really seen those girls, or was it all a pleasant dream? But I never saw them again.

I was brought back to reality when Sergeant Blaketon met me at my 7 a.m. point, and I wondered if he had driven out to meet me at six. But he said nothing about that missed rendezvous. He did, however, mention my dirty boots and my muddy trouser legs.

'I've been in the woods, sergeant,' I explained. 'I've had reports of a possible poacher or someone living rough,' and I outlined the reports I'd received.

'Good, keep up the good work, Rhea. Anything else to report?'

'No, it's all quiet, sergeant.'

'Good, well enjoy your walk. I'll get myself home for some breakfast. You can't beat an early start to the day – it sets the pulses racing. See you later.'

And that was it – until I chanced to see a girly calendar in a York shop the following Christmas. And there was my rock, the chair-shaped rock by the lake, with a beautiful blonde girl draped upon it, breasts and body bared for all the world to view. There was a total of twelve superb colour pictures, one for each month, and each was a woodland scene. I recognized eight of them – all eight had been photographed in those woods.

I saw from the credits that the photographer was a local man called Anthony Gourlay from York; it was then that I realized who the mysterious visitor had been. The sketchy descriptions I'd received did match his general appearance. I felt sure the mystery man had been Gourlay, reconnoitring the landscape in the morning light before deciding upon his precise locations for his calendar.

I did not tell anyone about this. After all, I did not want the lake to become a tourist attraction.

That brief but very pleasant experience highlighted the fact that our waterways, whether in the form of the seaside or inland rivers, lakes or ponds, can hold a promise of untold bliss. This is recognized by many. If there is a convenient stretch of water, the British will spend time beside it, even if only for a day. Yorkshire's dramatic coastline, its huge rivers and countless streams or becks, all bear witness to this longing for waterside leisure, especially during the summer when the people evacuate their cities and towns for a day beside the sea, a picnic near a moorland stream or a holiday beside a river or lake. It was an appreciation of our inbred escapist needs that persuaded a local farmer to make good use of some derelict buildings.

He was Arthur Fewster of Riverside Farm, Lower Keld. This remote Ryedale hamlet is a couple of miles west of Crampton and overlooks the gentle River Rye. It has no shop, post office or pub and is known for its underground springs, the Yorkshire word 'keld' meaning a spring. Much of the district's domestic water supply is pumped from Lower Keld's never-ending flow of deliciously crisp and pure water. I had very few reasons to call at any of the half-dozen houses which comprised Lower Keld, but did visit the farm each quarter to check Arthur's stock registers.

After one visit, where I had indulged in the 'lowance, i.e. the usual mid-morning snack of teacakes, fruit cake, cheese and biscuits, washed down by a huge mug of hot tea, Arthur said, 'Here, Mr Rhea, Ah'll show you summat.'

He led me across his spacious yard to what had been an old disused and tumbledown building, full of farmyard junk. Now it was sparkling with new paint and freshly pointed brickwork. There were five new doors, all glistening with fresh paint, and the windows shone in the morning sunshine. He opened one of the doors and led me inside; the transformation was astonishing.

There I saw a neat kitchen with a newly fitted sink and

cooker, and it was furnished with new pine chairs and a table. Two easy chairs stood in the far corners while a narrow wooden staircase rose from the floor. He led me into a small upstairs room and there I saw a double bed, a wardrobe, dressing-table and two easy chairs, all in fashionable pine. A small bathroom and toilet completed the accommodation.

'Holiday cottages,' he said proudly. 'Ah've converted this awd tile shed into five cottages, two doubles like this 'un, and three singles. T'other double's at yon end, singles are in t'middle. Fishermen, tha knows. They come for a weekend or longer, so Ah thowt Ah'd convert this awd spot into rooms for 'em. What do you think, Mr Rhea?'

'A great idea, Arthur,' I enthused. 'You've done a good job.'

'One day, farmers'll have to do summat other than farm, Mr Rhea,' he said. 'What with folks getting more leisure time and longer holidays, well, it makes sense to me to cater for 'em. Ah've done it all proper, planning consent and all that. So if you know anybody who's looking for a quiet spot beside the river, well, just you give 'em my name and address.'

'I will,' I promised him.

Arthur began to advertise his holiday accommodation, with special emphasis upon the opportunities for angling in this lovely river, and I did pass details to one or two people who inquired. I was later to learn they had been very happy in Arthur's old tile shed. He sold them fresh farm produce such as milk, eggs, potatoes and vegetables and they thought they were living the life of a rustic yokel. For some townies, the tile shed represented bliss of a kind not associated with city streets and concrete gardens. Arthur had hit upon a winner.

But from a police point of view, the assemblage of total strangers in an alien environment, where they must live and sleep in close proximity to one another, can often lead to problems. Police officers in holiday resorts are well aware of this and although I welcomed Arthur's initiative, I did wonder when there would be trouble at t'tile shed. I forecast someone going off without paying, or someone getting drunk and smashing Arthur's furniture or someone fighting with his neighbour over parking places, girl friends or something equally silly.

But I think Arthur must have chosen his guests very carefully because I received no complaints, either from the few villagers who lived nearby, or from Arthur or his guests. As time went by, the old riverside tile shed did appear to be a genuine haven of rural delight.

The fact that, when full, the tile shed accommodated only seven people might have had some bearing upon this happy state of affairs. Had it accommodated seventy, then there may have been occasions for aggravation. But even so, for some forty weeks of the year, Lower Keld's population was swollen quite considerably. The entire hamlet had less than twenty residents, and so Arthur's enterprise regularly increased its population by about a third. It was a large percentage increase, if a modest numerical one. The shop and pub in nearby Crampton approved and so the situation was never a problem.

That state of bliss continued until I received a telephone call from Miss Neville, a retired spinster of uncertain years whose cottage was very close to Arthur's tile shed.

'Mr Rhea,' she breathed into the telephone late one night, 'do come to Lower Keld, please. I'm sorry to ring so late, but I fear there is trouble at Arthur's tile shed and he is out, you see, with his wife. There is an awful noise and lots of arguing with people shouting. It's terrible, it really is most out of character. I do fear there is trouble.'

'I'll be there in ten minutes,' I assured her.

I'd just completed a late route and was in my office writing up my pocketbook when her call came, otherwise I might have been in bed. I noticed it was approaching 11.30.

'I'm just popping down to Lower Keld,' I called to Mary who was already in bed. 'I won't be long, it sounds like a domestic row in Arthur's holiday cottages.'

Domestic rows are an aggravating feature of a police officer's life. Where possible, we endeavour to avoid them because if we enter the fray (usually at the request of a

neighbour), the warring husband/wife/boy-friend/girl-friend/
lovers join forces and attack the peace-keeping constable. Our
attitude has always been that minor domestic wars are best left
to play themselves out in the family home, although we are
sometimes concerned about an outbreak of something more
serious, such as physical attacks or injuries.

So to what was I heading at Lower Keld? I wondered what
horrors lay before me. Domestics are never pleasant, they
seldom provide the slightest degree of job satisfaction....

In my little police van, I chugged along the lane towards the
tile shed, enjoying the peace of the late-night journey. When I
arrived at Riverside Farm, it was in darkness except for the
tile-shed block, and there I noticed lights in two of the units. I
knew that at this time of year, the early spring, things were
quiet; in fact, I was to learn that only two of the units were
currently occupied. I parked and walked through the gate and
into the courtyard, but there was no noise.

Two cars were parked there and I did see a light shining
from Miss Neville's cottage beyond the parking area; her
curtains fluttered as the gate clicked upon my entry, but she
had not ventured into the battleground to greet me. But when
I entered the paved courtyard, once a muddy portion of
Arthur's farmyard, I saw in the light cast from the units, two
silent figures lying on the stone flags. Had vile murder been
done?

I hurried to them, fearing the worst. To my surprise, I
found two women, both unconscious, and they were
surrounded by empty bottles ... gin bottles, Martinis, wine
bottles.

At first glance, I reckoned they'd be in their thirties. They
were casually dressed: one wore jeans and the other had a
short skirt; both wore thick sweaters. I checked their pulses
and listened to their breathing as I sought any signs of injury.
My brief examination convinced me that neither was hurt; the
problem was that they were very, very drunk.

I looked around for any indication of other trouble, but
found none, the only clue being that two chalet doors were

standing wide open, flooding their light into this courtyard.
Hurriedly, I entered the first and searched it, noting that the
single bed was unoccupied ... more empty bottles littered the
kitchen.

Next door, I knew, was the double chalet, the one I had
inspected with Arthur some time ago. Its door was also open
and the lights were on. I now entered that one, stepping
gingerly through the open door.

I walked past a pair of thigh-length waders and some fishing
equipment stacked in a corner, then went up the stairs. I
opened the bedroom door and was surprised to see a man on
one side of the bed, fast asleep. He was totally oblivious to the
situation outside and an empty malt whisky bottle stood on the
floor at the side of his bed.

From the available evidence, I could imagine what had
happened. The three of them had had a wild party with lots to
drink, and I guessed they'd been laughing and shouting
outside. Poor Miss Neville had misunderstood the situation;
she'd interpreted the noise as the sound of trouble whereas it
had been the sound of fun. There was no damage anywhere,
no injuries and no cause for alarm. Even so, it must have been
quite a party ... these three, friends by the look of it, had
enjoyed an almighty binge, but the two women had been
unable to regain their respective chalets. The husband had
managed to stagger upstairs with his bottle and had crashed
into bed. That was my assessment of the situation.

I could return each woman to her chalet, but which woman
should be sleeping with the man? I went upstairs to rouse him,
but failed. All my shouting and shaking had absolutely no
effect – the whisky had sent him into the deepest of sleeps. But
I could manage. I went outside and studied the drunken,
snoozing pair. For some reason I thought of Cinderella and
decided that shoes might provide the answer, so I went into
the single chalet and found a pair of high-heeled shoes.

I fitted them to each of the women's feet – they slid easily on
to the girl in the jeans, but were far too small for her
companion. The problem was solved! The next thing was to

get them to safety. I went into the double chalet and again tried to rouse the sleeping man, but with no success, and so I went to the girl wearing the mini-skirt, hauled her to her feet and slung her face down across my shoulder in the fireman's lift. It was a technique taught us at training school and it meant I could carry her quite easily.

She groaned a little and wheezed a lot while making other weird noises as I settled her on my shoulder with her head and arms hanging down my back. I clamped my arm around the back of her dangling legs, and in this way bore her into the chalet. I would drop her in bed beside her husband; it was the only safe and warm place. Without much trouble, I mounted the stairs, entered the bedroom and with my free hand, rolled back the sheets. The man was as naked as a new born babe. Then, as carefully as possible, I deposited the unconscious woman beside her unconscious husband; he groaned and turned to face her, still asleep, as she began to snore. Although she was fully dressed, I covered them and left them, dropping the Yale latch as I made my exit.

I repeated the exercise with the other woman, placing her fully dressed into her single bed, and then dropped her latch as I went out. I left each of their lights burning just in case they had to wander to the loo during the night.

And that was it. I was quite proud of the ease with which I had dealt with that little problem and turned to leave, only to find Miss Neville standing near the gate, clutching a coat about her.

'It was a party, Miss Neville, a somewhat drunken party by all accounts. They'll all in bed now, fast asleep.'

'I hope you didn't mind me calling ...'

'Not at all,' I assured her. 'That's what I'm here for.'

'I'll tell Mr Fewster when he returns, I think he and his wife are attending someone's silver-wedding party.'

'Yes, you tell him,' I smiled, looking at my watch. It was nearly quarter past twelve. 'But so far as I'm concerned, the matter is closed and I'm going home. Goodnight.'

It would be about ten o'clock next morning when a man

arrived at my police house. I welcomed him into my little office and settled him down. In his early forties with thinning sandy hair, he was smartly dressed in what were clearly a countryman's clothes – heavy greenish tweeds with brogue shoes bearing studded soles. He was smiling at me.

'You are the village constable, I understand?' he said in a gentle Scots accent. 'You patrol Lower Keld?'

'Yes, I'm PC Rhea,' I confirmed.

'I came to thank you,' he beamed. 'For last night.'

'Oh!' now I realized who he was and the purpose of his call.

'I saw Miss Neville this morning,' he enlightened me. 'She said she had called you, and that you had dealt with the problem.'

'It was nothing,' I assumed a modest pose. 'Just part of the service.'

'It was bloody good service if you ask me,' he chortled, his accent growing stronger. 'I go there to have a spot of quiet fishing, to get away from the pressures of work, you know, and what happens – some kind constable plonks a woman in bed beside me. I don't know her, and she doesn't know me … but what a time we had....'

'I thought she was your wife … '

'No, I have nae wife. I'm divorced. I spend my time fishing, it's relaxing. And last night, well, I drowned my sorrows with a good stiff whisky or two … but then I thought I was having a wonderful dream … stripping a woman, making love, it was some dream … then I woke up and found a woman at my side, naked, asleep … then she woke, saw me, screamed, grabbed her clothes and ran off … God knows where she went. But she was most friendly and co-operative during my dream, I can assure you … so I came to say thanks. Now, I'm going home feeling very happy and fulfilled – and I've had the best break of my life, thanks to you.'

When he'd gone, I pondered over the two women. Who was the one who'd entertained the fisherman? Some time later, I was talking to Arthur Fewster and referred to the incident.

He chuckled.

'By gum,' he grinned. 'You cheered that bloke up no end, Mr Rhea. Never had a time like it, he reckons. He asked if I could fix him up with another holiday like it.'

'But those two women ... I mean, I thought ... '

'Don't let it worry you, lad, no harm done. The one in my chalet comes from Brighton, t'other's her pal. The pal has a cousin in Lower Keld, Mrs Bayes down by t'bridge. She stayed there while her pal rented that spot from me. They'd had a bit of a farewell party last night ... now yon fisherman never locks his door. I reckon they'd strayed into his spot instead of hers when they were past caring ... that's why his door was open ... anyroad, it's all over. A good time was had by all.'

But I still do not know who that fisherman was, nor do I know the identity of his surprise partner that night.

But every Christmas for five or six years afterwards, a bottle of beautiful malt whisky would arrive at my house, anonymously. I raised my glass to him and to her, for she had made one man very happy and another very curious. Perhaps she is reading these words now?

I may never know.

★ ★ ★

That story of a strange party was echoed in another case which occurred in the hillside hamlet of Shelvingby, high on the southern escarpment of the North York Moors.

This tiny community of stone-built houses nestles deep in the moors beneath the sheltering slopes of a huge rounded hill. Once, not long ago, the village was the stronghold of local Methodism, John Wesley having preached here during one of his Yorkshire tours, and this might explain why the tiny village church reclines in the valley at a discreet distance from the village. Now, Methodism has virtually vanished from the district and the church is enjoying a revival, if only from visiting tourists. It stands beside the Shelf Beck, the village and beck being named after the strange step-like formation of the limestone landscape. In this case, the stream tumbles and roars down a series of stone shelves, but as it flows past the tiny church, it becomes calm and serene.

The churchyard borders the stream, and in late winter it is brilliant with masses of snowdrops; in the spring, it is the turn of the daffodils, for thousands of them bloom in this remote and quiet spot. Owing to its situation close to the beck, a public footpath passes through the churchyard, and consequently it is busy with hikers and ramblers for many weeks in the year. This does mean, however, that many passers-by pop into the church to contemplate its long history, and then they slip a coin or two into the offertory box. In this way, the little church enjoys a useful supplementary income.

It was a regular but local walker who drew my attention to a small problem in that churchyard. He was Timothy Pepper, a retired clerk.

A meek man, he had come to live in Shelvingby in his retirement. He was so meek and mild that when he heard strange noises emanating from the centre of the churchyard, he did not rush to investigate. Instead, he hurried home with his dog, an equally timid Yorkshire terrier called Garth, and wondered what to do about the noises. His wife, not eager to push Timothy to the limits of his valiant nature, advised him to forget it – it might have been nothing more than children playing or dogs skylarking. So Timothy obeyed her. For the next few weeks he walked his dog through the churchyard only during daylight hours, but as the autumn drew nearer, so the days grew darker.

Gradually, Timothy began to walk again in the darkness, but by now he'd forgotten about the noises and had resumed his night-time walks with Garth. Then around ten o'clock one night, he heard the noises again; he rushed home without seeking an explanation and this time his face was pale and his hair stood on end. Even Garth appeared to be worried about something because he refused to leave his master's side.

'It's awful,' Timothy stuttered to his wife. 'Terrible noises, shrieks ... weird laughter ... in the darkness ... '

'You're not telling me it's haunted?' Mrs Pepper was horrified at the possibility.

'No, I think it was humans,' he said. 'I wondered if there was some awful ritual being practised by incomers ... devil worship even, desecration of our churchyard or graves ... '

'It might be children playing,' she put to him.

'It didn't sound like children,' he said. 'Besides, it was late and we've no teenagers in this village, have we? One or two of infant school age, but it wouldn't be them, and there were no cars or motor bikes parked nearby ... '

Without an on-the-spot investigation by Timothy, it seemed that the cause of the noises would never be ascertained, and those who knew Timothy were quite aware of his shortcomings. When faced with an incident where positive action was required, Timothy would always seek someone else to take over. And so I was told of the problem during a routine visit to Shelvingby.

I popped into the shop, as was my practice, and was told all about Timothy's experience. I promised Mrs Belt, the shopkeeper, that I would keep an eye on the churchyard and I knew that news of my assurance would quickly reach the entire village. Shortly afterwards, when I came across Timothy taking Garth for his daily constitutional, I stopped my van and climbed out for a chat.

'I've heard about these noises in your churchyard, Mr Pepper,' I began. 'I thought I'd keep an eye on things. I've not heard them, so what can you tell me?'

He told me his story, but, after some prompting, did say that the noises were happy ones, like a party, with laughter and loud voices. But there were no lights. Most parties would have been illuminated by torches or lanterns, but he'd not seen such things.

He did say, however, that he was sure he'd heard a woman's voice, and added that he'd been to the centre of the graveyard in daylight but had seen no discarded bottles and no damage. The intruders did not seem to be vandals. On both occasions, the noises had occurred after 10 p.m.

'It's certainly mysterious,' I agreed. 'But thanks – I'll keep an eye open.'

Thereafter, each time I patrolled the village during the hours of darkness, I would leave the van at a discreet distance and take a walk along the public footpath which led to the churchyard. But on each occasion, I heard and saw nothing suspicious. After about four months, I had almost forgotten about the churchyard noises when I chanced to drive into Shelvingby late one night. I had no particular reason for being there but the village was on the route of one of my patrols. I parked in the village centre and walked around when, to my surprise, I saw Timothy making extreme haste towards me. He was dragging Garth by his lead and was clearly rushing about some urgent business – in fact, he was galloping home after undergoing another terrifying experience.

'Ah, Mr Rhea, thank God!' he panted. 'What a blessing I came across you ... those noises, they're there, now. I've just come from there....'

'Show me,' I requested. 'Then we can get the thing sorted out.'

'Oh, well, I ... er ... '

He was terrified, and so I didn't force him to accompany me; if the noises were still there, I would soon trace them. I took a powerful torch from my van and made my way to the graveyard; Timothy watched me for a few seconds, and then went home. On reflection, I'd be better without him – he might develop into a nervous wreck, faint on the spot or produce some other kind of problem. I walked towards the church with my soft-soled boots making no sound, and as I entered the churchyard I could hear some peculiar sounds. They were indeed coming from the midst of the gravestones, somewhere near the centre. I halted and listened.

It *did* sound like a party, albeit a small one, with a woman's voice laughing and talking. At this distance, the words were indistinct and I could not hear what she was saying, but as I stood and listened in the gloom of that October night, I could not see any lights nor could I discern the presence of any other people.

In some circumstances, particularly in such a location, the noises might frighten the faint-hearted, but police officers must not be afraid of the unknown, and so I moved quietly towards the sounds. On the soft grass between the tombstones my feet made no noise, and because my eyes had grown accustomed to the darkness I did not require my torch. Gradually, I moved closer to the noises, being guided by them. By now, they had been reduced to a softer chatter, as if the woman was talking to a friend.

I wondered if it was someone with a radio perhaps; a tramp maybe, sleeping rough, or some youngster seeking an opportunity to indulge in Radio Luxembourg after being forbidden to do so at home. But it was none of those.

As I approached, I could see a woman sitting against a tombstone, and she was alone. She was babbling away in her low voice and suddenly she shrieked with laughter, as if someone had told her a joke, and then she resumed her one-sided conversation. She had grey hair; I could see its light shade against the all-embracing darkness, and even now, as I stood only feet away, she was not aware of my presence.

I could see a bottle in her hand, a gin bottle I guessed, and all around the grave I could see beer bottles, empty ones. I had to make her aware of my presence and so I shone my torch. She blinked into the light, smiling up at me.

'Who's that?' her voice showed no fear, nor was she drunk.

'The policeman, PC Rhea from Aidensfield,' I said, switching off the light. 'I heard noises … '

'Sorry, officer,' she said. 'I was just having a drink … it's my husband's birthday, you see. We were just having a nice quiet drink together, and telling stories like we used to do … that's all.'

'I thought you were alone,' I could see no sign of her husband. 'So where's he?'

'Down here,' and she patted the earth beneath her. 'He's down here, and I've given him his eight pints … it's his birthday, you see, we always go out for a drink or two or three on his birthday, and on mine.... '

'So who are you?' I asked.

'Helen,' she said. 'Helen Brough. Alex's wife.'

I shone my torch on the gravestone and highlighted the inscription. I saw that the grave beneath her was that of Alexander Brough who had died three years earlier, aged sixty-four.

I did not know what to do with her. She was hardly drunk and disorderly; she was well dressed and she lived in the village, but she had this bizarre desire to drink at her husband's grave on celebratory occasions. And she made sure he got his share by pouring the contents of eight pint bottles on to his grave, but always removed the empties. I felt sure he would be happy with the arrangement – and he wouldn't have to stand anyone a round either!

My mind raced over the legislation I had been taught – I knew of the Ecclesiastical Courts Jurisdiction Act of 1860 which made brawling in a churchyard an offence. This was hardly 'brawling', i.e. any riotous, violent or indecent behaviour. She was not disturbing any divine service or troubling any minister or religion during divine service, although I did recall a provision which forbade the use of churchyards for secular purposes. Was she using it for a secular purpose by sharing a drink with her dead husband?

That, however, was not a police problem; it was the responsibility of churchwardens.

If she had been drunk, I might have considered the offence of being drunk and disorderly in a public place but she was not really disorderly, nor was she drunk and incapable, and it was questionable whether a graveyard at night was a public place.

I could think of no offences under the Noise Abatement Act, the Civic Amenities Act, the Litter Act, the Public Health Act, the Burial Act or the Burial Laws Amendment Act of 1880. The most likely offence was one under the Cemeteries Clauses Act of 1947 which made it illegal to play sports or games, or to discharge firearms (except at military funerals) or to commit any nuisance in a cemetery.

Was she committing a nuisance? What was a 'nuisance'?

I thought the wisest approach was to wait until someone made a formal complaint about her specific behaviour and then we would decide what to do about it. In the mean time, I told her to raise her glass to her husband and as she did, I said, 'Cheers, Alex,' then left.

As I have never received any formal complaint from the churchwarden or anyone else, Helen Brough might still be drinking with her husband on those private celebratory occasions. And I think the beer must have acted as a fertilizer because there was always a splendid crop of snowdrops on his grave.

2 *Stolen Sweets are Always Sweeter*

> What would be theft in other poets is only victory in him.
> John Dryden (1631–1700)

Theft is surely the most common of all crimes. It is committed by so many people in so many circumstances that it is impossible to record or even estimate an accurate total. The number of crimes known to the police bears little resemblance to the actual number committed, and this is particularly so where theft is concerned. Lots of us suffer thefts without reporting our loss to the police, either because we know the person responsible or we do not think any useful purpose would be served in making an official report.

There can be little doubt, however, that if every theft was reported to the authorities, then it would result in a more accurate and perhaps terrifying assessment of the nation's criminality. In that way, it might persuade the Home Office to permit police forces to recruit more constables in an attempt to combat the seemingly unstoppable growth of lawlessness. In spite of official denials, there is an acute shortage of uniformed, patrolling police officers.

As the village constable at Aidensfield, however, I was aware that my patch comprised a high proportion of law-abiding folk, but there were some felons among them.

Some operated stealthily while others were more open about their crimes; some got caught either by me or by their victims, but several did evade the majesty of the law. Some did not regard their thieving activities as either unlawful or even sinful, somehow convincing themselves that their actions were justified or not the action of a criminal. Many thieves do persuade themselves that they have a right to purloin their ill-gotten gains. Some shoplifters certainly think along those lines, but shoplifting is just one form of theft, and it is a serious crime with a maximum penalty of ten years' imprisonment.

I think it is fair to say that, in some cases, the act of stealing is an addiction – sometimes I wonder if there should be Thieves Anonymous just as there is Gamblers Anonymous and Alcoholics Anonymous. But the scheme would surely fail because thieves would steal from one another at their meetings....

Most police officers can give examples of compulsive thieves, people with the magpie mania. In Maddleskirk, for example, there was a milk roundsman who could not resist stealing things left in the yards and gardens of the houses to which he delivered his pintas. He had a penchant for children's trikes, but as the villagers all knew of his weakness, they never reported his crimes. They simply went to his house and reclaimed their missing goods. He stole anything and everything he could carry home, his range of trophies varying from zinc horse troughs to garden tools via trikes.

If it was left out in the open, Gold Top Gareth would pinch it. He never sold or disposed of his ill-gotten goods, and so it seems it was a genuine addiction.

But can theft ever be justified? For example, is it wrong for a man to steal a loaf of bread when he is starving? Is it wrong for him to steal a loaf for another man who is starving? This type of question is guaranteed to produce argument and discussion, with Robin Hood being quoted as an example of the merits in stealing from the rich to provide for the poor.

Such a Robin Hood type of character did operate on my beat, and I nicknamed him the Pilfering Poet. His crimes were never really serious, but they were annoying and, of course, they did not improve my crime statistics. Furthermore, they made my crime detection returns look positively sick!

The Poet's first reported crime was the theft of some hens. I was called to the premises of a poultry farmer at Elsinby and he led me to one of his henhouses. It stood in a large field some distance from the farmhouse and was one of dozens of similar wooden structures upon the premises. Jonathon Murray of Whin Bank Farm showed me the scene of the crime. He had locked up his hens the previous night at dusk, but when he'd come to let his birds out that morning, there was only one left in this particular henhouse. The door was closed and it was evident that the raid had occurred during the night. He'd lost twenty-three Rhode Island Red crossed with Light Sussex hens.

Hens of this breed were famed as good layers, but of that henhouse-full, only a solitary bird remained, clucking with pleasure at his arrival.

But the thief or thieves had left a curious note. It was hanging on the door and read,

> *We've taken your hens to feed the poor*
> *But we've left you one to breed some more.*

It was written in blue ballpoint pen on lined writing paper and hung from a hook inside the door. I took it down and asked,

'Any idea whose writing this is, Jon?'

'Nay, Mr Rhea.' He had lived on these premises all his life as man and boy, and shook his grey head. 'No idea.'

'And your other henhouses?'

'All present and correct, Mr Rhea. They've not raided any o' them.'

'Have you had any other hens stolen recently?'

Again he shook his head, 'Nay, lad. Never a one.'

I searched the ground around the henhouse for indications of any unusual boot prints or other clues, but found nothing. We returned to the farmhouse where Betty Murray produced three plates of scones and cakes, with a mug of coffee apiece, and I waded through this mammoth 'lowance break as I took written details of the crime. I kept the poetic note and promised I'd do my best to find the culprits.

Although the note was couched in royal 'we' terms, I suspected the thief was a lone operator. I had no idea why I felt this but later thefts reinforced that original gut-feeling. Jonathon did not honestly feel he'd get his birds back, but had had the sense to let me know about the crime in case similar ones were occurring nearby. But there weren't any others. I'd had no poultry thefts reported for some time, certainly none with this particularly poetic *modus operandi*. I made the usual inquiries at butchers' shops, hotels and other likely outlet points, but produced a blank. Nobody had seen Jonathon's poultry, dead or alive, dressed or undressed.

The next poetic theft was from the garden of a retired agricultural mechanic called Clive Gill. His garden was always a showpiece for he grew and exhibited a range of splendid flowers, specializing in chrysanthemums and dahlias. In his retirement, he produced gorgeous blooms which were in demand at weddings, funerals and every kind of special occasion.

Everyone liked Clive; he was a most friendly and jolly man. He rang me at nine one morning.

'Mr Rhea,' he said in his slow voice, 'you wouldn't believe this, but somebody's pinched my best spade. It's a stainless steel one, worth a few quid of anybody's money ... '

'Are you sure?' was my first question. 'You've not lent it to anyone, have you? Or put it in a different place?'

'No, nowt like that. In fact, the thieves have left a daft note behind ... '

'I'll come straight away,' I promised him. Already, I had the feeling that this would reveal another of those poetic MOs. I was right.

Clive lived in a delightful stone-built roadside cottage between Aidensfield and Elsinby and so I walked the mile or so, enjoying the sparkle of the mild spring morning. I spotted a wren busy with his nest building; a woodpecker hammering at an elm and a weasel darting across the road ahead of me. I arrived at Clive's cottage just before 9.30 and his wife greeted me. Pretty with her rimless spectacles and round, rosy face, she was a modest, tiny lady in her early sixties whose skills with flower arranging were invariably in demand at the local churches and chapels. She was also a keen member of the WI and was always prominent at WI events.

'Clive's in his greenhouse, Mr Rhea,' and she pointed in the general direction. 'I'll have some 'lowance ready when you've done.'

I found him re-potting some young green plants, and I marvelled at his natural skills as he upturned the plant pots and tapped out the small growths before transferring them to larger ones. He never spilt a bit of soil – I'd have had soil all over the floor if I'd been attempting that.

'There's the note, Mr Rhea,' he nodded towards a shelf at the other side of his greenhouse. I found a note on lined writing paper, written in blue ballpoint pen. This one said,

> *We've taken your spade, your garden is weedy*
> *we'll make sure it's used to till for the needy.*

'They've a bloody cheek,' he said. 'My garden's never weedy!'

I asked the usual questions about where he'd left the spade, what it looked like and whether he recognized the handwriting of the note, and then adjourned to the house for a hefty bout of eating Mrs Gill's sumptuous 'lowance. In addition to everything else, she produced a delicious slab of apple pie and this kept me busy as I compiled my crime report.

'If they'd wanted an old spade for the needy, I could have given 'em one,' Clive said. 'I've dozens in my shed, but that was my best 'un, a newish 'un, an' all.'

I told him about the missing hens and their note, and promised I'd do my best to recover his lost spade, albeit with little confidence in my own ability to retrieve it. Even if I did find it, it would be difficult proving its true ownership.

Looking at the poem, I realized once more that the note was couched in the plural and I began to wonder about the identity

of the poor and needy who were recipients of this odd selection
of stolen property. Were the goods genuinely being handed
over for some charitable purpose, or was this just a poetic ploy
by the thief or thieves?

Within the next few months, more stolen goods vanished at
the hand of the mysterious poet. A fruiterer lost some of the
stock from his wagon and this note was left:

> *Apples, pears and plums galore,*
> *We've given them away, you can get some more.*

A lady who had been spring cleaning her cottage had left a
kitchen chair outside the back door. She intended taking it to
a local upholsterer for repairs to its cane seat. One night, the
chair vanished and a note said:

> *The chair you left outside your door*
> *Will come in handy for someone poor.*

A greengrocer discovered that part of his delivery of fresh
vegetables, left outside his shop doorway in the early hours by
the wholesaler, had vanished. The note said:

> *We've taken some peas and artichokes*
> *To be used in soup for our old folks.*

When a florist found several vases of display flowers missing
at Ashfordly, a note was left which said:

> *Your lovely flowers will cheer the room*
> *Of one who has to live alone.*

In many cases, the stolen goods were items of food or
associated with food. Without exception, the victims said that
if the thieves had only asked, they would have willingly
donated the items, or something similar, if it would ease the
plight of someone less-well-off than themselves. None could
understand why the thieves bothered to steal goods which
would have been freely donated.

Within a space of about nine months, dozens of these minor thefts occurred, the hallmark of each one being the poetic MO.

My Pilfering Poet was certainly causing me a headache, but not once did I get any clue as to his identity; no one had seen or heard anything which might lead to him, her or them.

No vehicles had been heard or seen at odd hours, although it did seem that the crimes were the work of someone who was around at night, or in the very early hours of the morning. I did wonder if it was a driver regularly passing through the district, someone who was not local. My colleagues and I made inquiries at all the charitable and welfare organizations in the locality in the hope that we might identify the destination of the stolen goods, but we produced no information. The handwriting was never identified, while the writing paper could have come from any cheap pad.

Then, as suddenly as he had started, the Pilfering Poet ceased his activities. For weeks, no more notes were left and I wondered if it was someone who had moved from the district, or if the travelling pilferer had had his route altered. But I had to submit progress reports to show that I was continuing to investigate the crimes. Then, just before one month's end, I got the following note from Sergeant Bairstow:

> *The Inspector hopes you'll make the time*
> *To trace the suspect of your poetic crime.*

I decided to enter the spirit of the occasion and submitted the following progress report:

> *I've made inquiries all around*
> *But not a single clue I've found.*
> *The crimes all happened in the night*
> *With victims safely out of sight.*
> *Done with guile and some great stealth*
> *To benefit those who lack the wealth*
> *To make their own ends meet with ease.*
> *From garden spades to tins of peas –*
> *The range of thefts is quite bizarre*

But no one's seen or heard a car
Or van or bike or other steed
To carry spoils to those in need.
Our villain's silent, clever and shrewd
I think it must be Robin Hood.

I did not receive any response to my own modest poetic effort, but neither did I trace that thief or thieves.

★   ★   ★

All criminals use an MO. The Pilfering Poet's MO was his habit of leaving behind a suitable verse. The initials MO mean *modus operandi*, which translated into English is 'method of operation'. In many cases, it is possible to identify a criminal through his or her MO; some burglars, for example, always break in through a rear window, some use an upstairs window, some climb fall pipes and break in through a bedroom window. Some smash their way in while others drill holes in the woodwork of windows; some use master keys.

Others always have a meal in the attacked house, some write graffiti on walls, while highly nervous types will pee or do worse on the floor or carpet. Many a burgled householder has found a heap of stinking excrement on their finest rug – and it wasn't left by the dog.

Just as each of us has our own way of doing things, whether it is cleaning the house, performing our routine tasks like dressing ourselves or locking up at night, so villains all adopt a pattern in their crimes, often without realizing it. This enables the police to identify a criminal, even if, at times, it is not possible to prove his or her guilt.

One example was a local burglar with a very curious MO. He rejoiced in the unlikely name of Octavius Horatio Calpin and came from a very good but very large family in Ashfordly. As his name suggests, Octavius was the eighth child; the seventh was Septimus Brutus while the sixth was Sixtus Cletus, but I never did learn the name of their earlier brothers and sisters. However, his younger sister, the tenth in the family, was called Decima Prudence.

For some reason, Octavius turned out to be a wrong 'un. Even at school, when aged only six and three-quarters, he was caught stealing sweets and dinner money from his classmates, and when he persisted with his dishonesty in later years, his actions puzzled everyone. The family, local farmers, oozed love and affection for all their children, they were well fed and decently clothed and were among the happiest of people.

Octavius was the only one who went off the proverbial rails. What had persuaded him to turn to crime may never be known, but he did develop into a criminal of considerable skill. There was clearly some character defect, for outwardly he was a charming and likeable young man. As a criminal, he was fairly successful – by that I mean he was not often caught or prosecuted although we knew he was responsible for a high number of local housebreakings.

We became aware of his crimes through his MO. Octavius was a housebreaker and burglar, those two crimes being quite distinct from each other until the legal changes of 1968. Burglary was the name then given to the crime of breaking into someone's dwelling house *only at night*, i.e. between 9 p.m. and 6 a.m. If the house was broken into at any other time, the crime was classified as housebreaking and carried a lesser penalty. Other similar crimes were variously known as shopbreaking, garage breaking, office breaking, warehouse breaking and so forth. Since 1968, however, all such offences of breaking into property have been reclassified as burglary, whether or not the attacked premises were houses or other buildings.

In the main, Octavius tried to restrict his crimes to housebreaking, tending to enter good quality homes during the daylight hours while the occupants were away or at work. Very occasionally, he committed a burglary, but those crimes were rare – he knew the prevailing high penalties for burglary and rarely took that risk.

But his MO was rather peculiar. He insisted on tidying up

the houses which he entered. He did not merely tidy up his own mess, but tidied the entire premises, putting things straight. He would wipe the dust off shiny surfaces, place magazines and newspapers in a neat pile, pair off shoes, straighten pictures, replace jam jars and condiment sets in kitchen cupboards and perform a whole range of similar tidying-up routines.

This was in direct contrast to many other housebreakers who would smash up a house, spray paint on the walls and generally vandalize the premises to leave a terrible, heart-rending mess. On occasions, some of Octavius's victims reported things stolen when in fact they had been tidied away by their burglar – one lady reported the theft of a jar of marmalade, a packet of corn flakes and two china mugs because they'd vanished from her kitchen table. Later, she found them in a kitchen cupboard – Octavius had tidied them away.

He achieved most of this without leaving any fingerprints, but from time to time he did make mistakes, and in the months before my arrival at Aidensfeld, he had been arrested and sentenced to two years' imprisonment for housebreaking and theft. Thus he had a criminal record and, as a consequence, his fingerprints were on file.

For a time, Octavius went straight but eventually his old desires returned and we learned of this when a country house near York was raided and a large quantity of silver stolen.

The crime had all the hallmarks of a professional housebreaker, but the local police found something odd – the kitchen had been tidied up and papers on the desk of the occupier had been neatly re-arranged. From this, we knew the culprit was Octavius, but when his home was searched, nothing incriminating was found. He had speedily disposed of the proceeds. Other than the MO, we had no way of proving his guilt, and he denied responsibility. We knew we were now having to deal with a rather clever and professional criminal. His time in prison had taught him the doubtful skills of raiding a better class of house, as well as providing some useful

tips for avoiding conviction. Having served his apprentice-
ship, Octavius was now a professional.

Soon, other houses of quality were raided; antiques,
silverware, glassware and pottery, all of a high quality, were
stolen. In each case, the place was tidied up; in each case,
Octavius was questioned, and in each case, we were unable to
prove his guilt. He left no fingerprints, and no incriminating
evidence was ever found upon him or in his possession.
Octavius's time in prison had been very well spent – it had
been his University of Crooked Skills.

The local CID, crime prevention officers, crime squads and
detectives from neighbouring forces held a meeting to pool
their ideas to 'target' Octavius Horatio Calpin. One outcome
was that all rural beat officers, like myself, were issued with
information about the scale of Octavius's crimes.

We had instructions to alert all the occupiers of large
country houses and stately homes on our beats. I had several
on my patch, some occupied and owned by national figures
and some containing very valuable sculptures, paintings and
antiques. I decided to visit each in turn and advise their
owners to be more security conscious. I issued leaflets and
drew attention to the vulnerable points of their homes, calling
in specialist crime prevention officers where appropriate.

One of the householders was Sir James Schofield, who lived
at Briggsby Manor on the north-west corner of my patch.
With interests in brewing, horse-racing and property
development, he and Lady Schofield owned a beautiful home
set among trees on the outskirts of Briggsby. It overlooked
Briggsby Beck, a delightful moorland stream which rippled
across a rocky bed as it flowed into the Rye. I made an
appointment to visit Sir James and upon my arrival was shown
into his richly furnished study. A maid brought coffee and
biscuits on a silver tray, inviting me to help myself as I awaited
the master of the house. He arrived in a good mood, his
cheerful grey eyes smiling at me as he poured himself a coffee.
He sat behind his large desk, his small figure almost concealed
by its bulk, but his personality was large and happy.

'So,' he boomed in a voice far louder than anyone would have expected. 'What brings the constabulary to Briggsby Manor?'

I explained my purpose, alarming him with stories of burglaries and housebreakings in houses similar to his own, and voicing our belief that one man was responsible. I told him a little about Octavius. I advised him on security, on the need for window locks and for care by his staff whenever they retired for the night or vacated the house. He listened and thanked me, then said, 'But I have a good alarm, Mr Rhea, for my cash and my wife's jewellery. Here, I'll show you. But first, let me de-activate it.'

He took me into the hall where he pressed the switch to cut off the alarm, then I followed him into the massive drawing room with its polished wooden floors. I admired the huge open fireplace, the oak panelling and the sumptuous furnishings as he led me to an oil painting on the south wall. He lifted it up and beneath was a wall safe.

'Total security,' he said proudly. 'Not even a thermal lance would get into that – and if anyone does try, the alarm will go off. It's a silent alarm; it's linked to your headquarters so that if a burglar does come here, your officers will be alerted without the criminal being aware of it. And so, God willing, you'll catch him.'

I realized that a lot of luck was needed – a patrolling officer would have to be in the vicinity if he was to catch a villain quickly, but it was not impossible. Sometimes luck could be on our side. I explained to Sir James that he had many other valuables that could not be accommodated in that safe. These included his many pictures, his antiques, his everyday items like TV set, binoculars, radio and so forth; they were all valuable and so he promised he'd review his overall security arrangements. Having shown me the wall safe behind the coaching scene, which was some three feet long by two feet deep, he replaced the picture.

'Sir James,' I asked, 'how is that alarm activated? The one that protects the wall safe?'

'By the slightest movement of this picture,' he said. 'That's why the alarm must be switched off when the maid dusts it.'

'So if someone tried to straighten the picture when the alarm was set, it would react and issue a warning?'

He was quick to see my plan.

He smiled. 'So if I leave this picture slightly skew-whiff, you think your tidy-minded housebreaker might attempt to straighten it? And set off the alarm? And so get himself arrested?'

'Yes,' I said. 'If he comes here … I've no information that he will attempt to break into your property, Sir James, but you are vulnerable and well, it would be nice to catch him red-handed.'

'I'll leave that picture out-of-true,' he laughed. 'I'll tell my staff not to touch it. It'll be a good story at the club if we do nail him, eh?'

And so the trap was set.

There were two further raids on country houses within the next five months, and then one evening when I was on patrol in my official mini-van at Stovingsby, I received a call over my radio. The alarm at Briggsby Manor had been activated – intruders were on the premises. I knew Sir James and Lady Schofield were away at Cheltenham races for the Gold Cup and so the house would be unoccupied because the staff lived out in their own homes. The intruder had known this. The call instructed all mobiles to attend Briggsby Manor but not to arrive like a cavalry charge with flashing blue lights and a lot of noise. If there was an intruder, we must catch and detain him through stealth and cunning. I reckoned I was nearest but I was alone, and it is difficult for one police constable to surround a mansion as large as Briggsby Manor and to supervise all its exits.

I was more than relieved, therefore, to hear the call-sign of a CID car which was just leaving Ashfordly Police Station with two detectives on board. They had heard the call and were on their way. I suggested a rendezvous point out of sight of the manor, and said that as I was familiar with the grounds and the layout of the house, we could probably arrest our raider red-handed. Without going into a lot of detail, we did just that. In the darkness, we found the break-in point and chummy's parked van; we waited and jumped on him while he was in possession of a suitcase full of silverware. And, as expected, it was our friend Octavius Horatio Calpin.

He had been unable to resist straightening the crooked picture and had consequently trapped himself. We never told him how we had trapped him – we knew we could set the same trap again, at some future date when he got out of prison because, as sure as God made little thieves, Octavius would go a-burgling and a-housebreaking in the future. And, because his long-suffering mum, with all her children, had insisted that each of them tidied his own room, so Octavius would tidy up some future house in which he found himself, lawfully or not. I wondered what sort of job they would give him in prison – whatever it was, he'd certainly leave the place tidier than when he arrived.

For the crime at Briggsby Manor, he was sentenced to five years' imprisonment which meant he had a long time to get the prison as tidy as he wished.

*   *   *

Surely the strangest thief was a scruffy individual in his mid-forties who lived alone in a prefab in Crampton. He had no regular work and described himself as a general dealer; we called him a scrappie for he dealt in all kinds of scrap junk and waste metal which he collected in an old van.

Over a wide area he was known as Tin Lid Talbot. His real name was James Edward Talbot, but very few knew that, for he had earned his nickname through hoarding a bewildering range of old tin lids. They fitted everything from oil drums and dustbins to tea-pots, kettles and jam jars.

As police officers, we knew he was not against the occasional bout of petty thieving; if he called at a house or farm and there was no one about, he would steal things from the premises.

Usually, it was stuff that the owner was glad to get rid of but from time to time he would overstretch their generosity to make off with cash or something of real value. And then we would call on him. As a consequence, he was one of the regulars at the local magistrates' court, somehow avoiding any custodial sentence, but invariably being put on probation or being fined small sums, which never deterred him. I think the Bench felt sorry for him; he wasn't really a criminal, not in the nasty sense of the word, for his thieving was mainly restricted to things he found lying about and which were considered almost useless. Furthermore, he would never, for example, break into a house or outbuilding nor would he dream of using violence against anyone or anything.

He would, however, sneak into a house if the door was standing open and take whatever he found inside – and in the country districts, people did leave their doors open with money placed ready for collection by people like the insurance man, the milkman and catalogue collectors. Sometimes, the available cash was a temptation for Tin Lid and he would take it.

As a result, he had a huge list of petty convictions and a friendly relationship with the magistrates, the clerk of the court and the prosecuting officer. I think they all felt vaguely sorry for Tin Lid Talbot.

He was a pathetic fellow really, with his unkempt, lank and dark greasy hair, his mouth full of bad teeth, his dirty finger nails, clothes which were always too large for his small figure, plus his eternal wellington boots which he wore even in summer. But his long list of convictions was due largely to his strange response when questioned by the police – he would always deny his guilt while simultaneously but unwittingly admitting it. If that seems odd, I can give the first example I encountered.

A company director called Owen Robertson rang me to complain that his garden roller had been stolen. It was a large roller in good condition and it had been taken from his front lawn. A vehicle was obviously required to carry it off. When I interviewed him, he said the house had been visited by Talbot's General Dealers that very afternoon – he knew this, because Tin Lid had left a printed note to that effect.

The note said that if the housebuilders had any surplus metal, Mr Talbot would be glad to call and take it away. I drove straight to Tin Lid's old shack; his van was there and I saw a plank still in position, leading from the rear to the ground. It was just the thing for the removal of a garden roller. I found him in his shed and, knowing how to deal with him, said, 'Now, Tin Lid. What have you done with Mr Robertson's garden roller?'

'Not me, Mr Rhea,' he shook his dirty head.

'You called this afternoon and stole it,' I said.

'Look, do you think I've taken it to roll my mother's lawn or something?'

His equally scruffy mother, in her dotage, lived in similar conditions next door and so I went through the gate. And there was the roller on her lawn. He hadn't even had the time to use it.

'Come along, Tin Lid, back into your van with it, and take it straight back to where it belongs. Now! This very minute.'

'Yes, all right, Mr Rhea, but I just wanted to borrow it … '

'Then you should have asked,' I said. I helped him to roll it up the plank and we secured it in the back of his old van, then I followed him to Mr Robertson's house. Robertson declined to prosecute. He felt sorry for the pathetic little figure standing before him and was just happy to have his roller back. Tin Lid was lucky on that occasion.

Over the years, I assembled a catalogue of his curious denials. Once, he stole some cash from an unlocked house – it was £5 left out for the insurance man by a lady in Aidensfield. She'd left her door standing open when Tin Lid happened to be visiting the village, and he'd been tempted. When I interviewed him, he said, 'Not me, Mr Rhea. Do you think I'd steal her fiver and spend it in the pub or something?'

When I saw George Ward, the landlord of the Hopbind Inn at Elsinby, he recalled Tin Lid entering to buy drinks and using a £5 note for the purpose.

Tin Lid was fined £3 and ordered to pay restitution for that episode.

On another occasion, a fine brass coach lamp disappeared from a builder's yard in Maddleskirk. The builder, John Grant, had bought it to embellish his own front door and had left it unattended for twenty minutes while he took a phone call. In that time, Tin Lid had entered the yard, seen the lamp and taken it. As it was known he was collecting scrap in the village at that time, I found myself driving to his yard once again.

'It's about a lovely brass coach lamp, Tin Lid,' I announced. 'Taken from Grant's yard in Maddleskirk this morning. What have you done with it?'

'Not me, Mr Rhea,' he said. 'You don't think I'd take a thing like that and sell it to an antique dealer, do you?'

I recovered it from an antique shop in Ashfordly, and on this occasion Tin Lid was fined £5.

I do know that other officers had occasion to interview him and they all knew of his strange form of denial, but, from my own view point, I found this quirk of character to be most fascinating. He never did learn any other way of denying his guilt and over the years he told me a succession of stories like:

'You don't think I'd steal a thing like that and hide it up my chimney, do you, Mr Rhea?'

'You don't think I'd nick a pile of tiles like that and bury them in the garden, do you, Mr Rhea?'

'You don't think I'd steal milk money from a doorstep and put the cash on a horse or something, do you, Mr Rhea?'

'You don't think I'd steal a spare wheel and put it on my own van, do you, Mr Rhea?'

'You don't think I'd steal a coil of rope from that cow shed and use it as a tow rope or something, do you, Mr Rhea?'

'You don't think I'd stoop to stealing a Christmas tree, then give it to the children's home, do you, Mr Rhea?'

If his denials had not been so pathetic, they would have been funny, and I know that all of my colleagues could tell similar stories about dear old Tin Lid. But the inevitable happened. He was arrested by a new detective because he was suspected of stealing seventeen dozen clay plant pots in assorted sizes. It was alleged he had taken them from a garden centre he'd visited on his scrap round, but they were not to be found anywhere. Most certainly, they were not on his premises.

I became aware of this when visiting Eltering Police Station because I saw his name in the charge book. He was then reclining in the cells, having been unsuccessfully interrogated by the new detective, a man called Littleton. Sergeant Bairstow hailed me.

'Nick,' he said. 'We've got Tin Lid down the cells, he's been lifted for nicking some plant pots but denies it. Littleton's sure he's our man, but he's admitting nothing.'

'Was he caught with the stuff?' I asked.

'No, and it's not on his premises.'

'Then why involve me?' I asked with interest.

'You know him, have a word with him for us. He talks to you. Get him to admit the job, that's all. Take a voluntary from him, then we can wrap this case up. When he coughs, we'll release him on bail.'

I read up the case papers and learned that Tin Lid had been seen near the garden centre in question; furthermore, he had been there around the material time and he'd been in possession of his van. It did seem possible that he was the culprit and it was the sort of thing he'd do, although I suspected he'd be content with one plant pot rather than two hundred. Full of curiosity, I went into his cell, taking with me a cup of hot sweet tea.

'Now then, Tin Lid,' I said, sitting on the hard bed at his side. 'What's all this about you stealing plant pots?'

'Not me, Mr Rhea. I never touched 'em. I was near that spot, I'll admit that, but I never took the pots.'

'I believe you, Tid Lid,' I said.

I went out and told Sergeant Bairstow that in my opinion, Tin Lid was not guilty – I knew that because he had not delivered his usual strange denial. That omission convinced me. I don't think that either Littleton and Bairstow

immediately accepted my view for each went into the cell to
re-interview Tin Lid, but he never admitted that theft.

I do know that Sergeant Bairstow spoke to Tin Lid in words
to the effect that, 'If PC Rhea believes you, Tin Lid, it's good
enough for me.'

He was released without charge. Next day, he was passing
my police house when he halted and knocked at my door.

'Hello, Tin Lid, this is a surprise!'

It was, because he never volunteered to visit the police.

'You told them you believed me yesterday, Mr Rhea,' he
said. 'You know an honest man when you see one. I'm not a
copper's nark, Mr Rhea, but the chap that pinched those pots
is Sacky Conway from Eltering. That's my way of saying
thanks.'

'Thanks, Tin Lid.' I invited him in for a cup of coffee, but
he said he had to dash off. I rang Sergeant Bairstow who was
on duty at Eltering and gave him the tip.

'Thanks, Nick. Somebody tipped you off, eh?'

'An old friend, serge,' I said. 'A chap who just can't tell a
lie!'

3   Artful Deceivers

Of wiles more unexpert, I boast not
John Milton (1608–74)

When it comes to the practice of dishonesty and deceit, the human being shows extraordinary skill. It is a fact of life that some very shrewd and clever people turn to dishonesty as a livelihood or hobby, and one wonders what satisfaction they achieve by denying others their lawful and rightful ownership of goods or services. Criminals are usually very selfish people.

Police officers are very aware that where money is involved and where any new thief-proof procedure is developed, some cunning rogue will devise a method of beating the system in order to steal. Their cunning is legendary. Nothing is foolproof; no procedure or security system is totally secure against the wiles of a cunning and persistent criminal, and society will always have to tolerate dishonest people.

I've come across seemingly meek old ladies who were skilled shoplifters; I've come across people who never paid their grocery bills or other debts – and in these cases, the police are powerless to act because these are civil debts.

But sometimes I wonder if the criminal law and its interpretation of the word 'dishonesty' should now apply to those who deliberately obtain goods or services with no intention of paying. One's actions are often proof of one's intent and where a person regularly and systematically defrauds tradespeople of their just monies, then surely a crime is committed?

It is a sad fact too that so many dishonest people appear to be trustworthy and as such are the last that anyone would suspect of roguish deeds. Examples of this occurred in two interesting cases on my patch at Aidensfield. Neither reached the courts for in both cases it was impossible to prove any breach of the criminal law, but the morals of each case were certainly of the lowest kind. For that reason, they are worthy of record.

The first involved a spinster lady called Penelope Stirling who was highly respected in Ploatby where she lived. A church organist, she arranged the ladies' flower rota and it was known she had worked in London before retiring to Yorkshire. She'd be in her early sixties when I moved to the area. Her home was a neat little detached house known as Miller's Cottage, and she ran a small, pale-blue Austin mini saloon. She was a fussy little person, always popping in and out of houses in Ploatby, Elsinby, Maddleskirk, Aidensfield and elsewhere, giving a helping hand to those less fortunate than herself.

When Meals on Wheels became so popular, it was Miss Stirling who volunteered to operate it in our district.

In short, Miss Stirling was a treasure, a wonderful volunteer helper in all kinds of ways, even if she was very prim and rather humourless. I became aware of her through her voluntary work for I'd noticed her going busily about her many social activities. In winter, she was very recognizable in her fur coat, fur hat with ear warmers and the curious fur muff which kept her hands warm. She wore heavy tortoiseshell spectacles, and when she was fully clad in her furs, all that I could see of her features was her sharp nose and rosy cheeks. She darted about the villages like a busy jenny wren. In summer, she wore a light-coloured belted raincoat and a plastic headcover.

She called at my house one day seeking donations for the Red Cross, and introduced herself. Afterwards, I often noticed her little car parked outside houses around my patch. Everyone spoke very highly of her – she shopped for the elderly and infirm, she ran errands for the sick, she dusted and tidied the homes of those unable to fend for themselves and took elderly ladies for trips into the countryside or to the seaside. The old folk all loved her and she demanded nothing in return. Her actions were entirely voluntary and done out of good will.

In spite of her help to others, I came to realize that Penny, as everyone called her, was a very lonely woman.

Although she visited the homes of so many people, I knew of none who had been invited into her house and none who had actually stepped inside. Even regular callers such as the milkman, the butcher and the insurance man had never been inside. She dealt with each on the doorstep. Her home life seemed sacrosanct and almost secretive.

Another intriguing factor was that I never saw her with any of her own family – she seemed to have no aged mother or father, no brothers or sisters, no visiting cousins. Even more curious for a woman in her position, was that there seemed none of that range of nephews and nieces who might call. Lots of maiden ladies had nephews and nieces who visited them. But Penny Stirling hadn't anyone; she was totally alone, and in time I realized she had neither a cat nor a dog. There was no living thing in her quiet home, apart from herself. I wondered if she was happy there.

I never did discover precisely what her occupation had been, other than she made it known she had worked in London; those to whom she had imparted this information assumed she had been employed in a big office somewhere, a civil servant perhaps, a top secretary or something similar.

Among her interests beyond social work was attending sales of furniture or house contents at local farms and cottages. These occurred on a fairly regular basis and I was usually informed by the auctioneers about an impending sale in case there was a traffic problem. Some farm entrances, for example, were on dangerous bends in the road, and, in some cases, house contents were displayed prior to the sale by making use of village greens, roadside verges and any available space. Minor problems could arise.

These sales were very popular, with one species of sale-goer being the city antique dealer who came into our villages in the hope of securing some hitherto unrevealed treasure. There is no doubt some did buy wonderful things – I once saw a book dealer flush with pride at buying a job lot of old books in a cardboard box. His earlier inspection had shown it to contain a rare old Bible. Auctioneers and buyers are full of such stories.

As I attended these sales, I became aware of Penny Stirling's familiar figure. She attended most and almost always bought something. She seemed to know her antiques, often buying glassware, china and books; I also noticed that she was most willing to purchase incomplete sets of objects. While most of us would wish to purchase a complete set of glasses, cutlery or books, Miss Stirling bought incomplete ones. At Elsinby one day, I saw her bid successfully for an incomplete set of the works of Charles Dickens. Two volumes were absent, and so the price was far lower than it would have been for the full set.

It was her purchase of that set of books that alerted me to her devious and highly suspect behaviour, because within a month I saw that same set of books for sale in a York shop.

This time, the set was complete. The missing volumes were present and I knew it was the same set because of the name inscribed in the front of each volume. Old folks would write their names inside their books and each of these contained the signature 'R.J. Stewart'. So where had the two missing volumes come from?

It was the contents of the Stewarts' home that had been sold recently, and at which Penny had bought the incomplete set. I knew, from local knowledge, that Penny had been caring for the old and widowed Mrs Stewart before her death, undertaking such chores as driving her to the shops, washing her clothes and cooking her meals.

My suspicious police mind began to operate and, for a time, I did wonder whether I was grossly wrong in my assessment of Penny's character and motives. I hoped I was; after all, she did do an enormous amount of charitable and beneficial work, but

I had to find out whether there was more to her – and I had to do so with the utmost discretion.

I was uncertain how to begin my inquiries, for I did not want to give even a hint of my suspicions to another soul. But providence was on my side because, within the month, another of Penny's 'patients' died and the contents of her house were put up for auction. She was Mrs Elsie Baker and I made a point of attending that sale.

Mrs Baker lived in a terrace-house in Aidensfield and, before her death, she had left instructions that her house and its contents be sold and the proceeds given to cancer research. She had not been a wealthy lady, but since her husband's death had kept a nice house with some interesting glassware. She had no immediate family who might inherit her belongings.

Having ensured there would be no obstruction of the highway due to the crowd and the furniture, I watched the proceedings. There was little of interest until some very fine engraved wine glasses were held aloft – and the auctioneer announced that it was an incomplete set. There were only two glasses instead of the required three. The bidding proceeded slowly and, sure enough, Miss Stirling was making her bids. I joined in with one or two bids, if only to push up the price she would pay to cancer research, but the glasses were knocked down to Penelope Stirling. I noticed the fierce glow of pride on her sharp features.

When it was all over, I managed to find a quiet corner for a chat with the auctioneer, Paul Sandford. I asked about the wine glasses.

'They're beautiful,' he said. 'I saw you bidding, but if that set had been complete, they'd have been worth much more.'

'Does Miss Stirling often buy incomplete sets of things?' I asked.

He glanced at me as if reading my mind or knowing of my suspicions, then said, 'She does. I must admit that over the years I've noticed her doing that. Sets of books, glassware, china objects, cutlery, condiment sets, candle sticks ... mainly household things you'd expect to find in complete sets. I can guarantee that if I offer an incomplete set of any worthwhile objects in this locality, she'll bid for it – and get it. Anyway, Mr Rhea, why are you interested in her deals?'

I told him about the Dickens volumes and of Penny's charity towards those whose goods were later put up for auction. I decided to voice my suspicions to him. 'I think she's borrowing things from those people while they're alive – and not returning them. She's doing so when she knows they'll soon go to meet their heavenly maker, and then she goes to the auction to buy the rest of the goods. She then makes up a complete set and trades it in for a massive profit. She's clever, Mr Sandford. She's too crafty to remove the entire sets because that would raise questions.'

'People aren't as devious as that, surely!' he protested.

'They can be,' I assured him.

'If it's true, what can we do about it?' he asked. 'There's nothing illegal in borrowing things, is there? And if the owner dies before the object is returned, so what?'

'Precisely!' I said.

'I'll keep an eye on her,' he promised. 'If she is doing that, she's denying lots of relations and other benefactors their dues. And as we handle most of the local auctions, I can check her easily enough. Pop in to my saleroom when you've time to spare and we'll have a look at the records of some recent sales.'

It was several months later when I called, his commitments and mine conspiring to prevent us meeting earlier. There had been no further local house content sales in that time, and when I settled before his old desk, it was clear he had already done his own research.

'I've checked back several years,' he said. 'We keep detailed records of our sales and, in the past four years, your Miss Stirling has regularly bought part sets of all manner of things. There is a definite pattern – she obviously knows her antiques and knows exactly what to buy. As we said earlier, it's chiefly domestic stuff – glasses, cutlery, volumes of books and so forth. She seems to know when the person is going to die because I remember one or two families' relations asking where certain items had gone – they'd visited their aunts, mothers, dads or whatever shortly before their deaths and some had noticed things were missing. The old folks couldn't remember what they'd done with them – in fact, I do wonder if that woman was taking them without the knowledge of her old folks. But she does seem to know the very personal circumstances of each old person and whether there will be a future sale of house contents – it's often folks who have no dependent relatives or those who want to donate something to charity.'

'It wouldn't surprise me if she was systematically stealing from the old folk,' I ventured. 'Being a so-called friend, she could take away bits and pieces without them knowing or being suspicious about her motives. She could do that by asking to borrow things – everybody does it.'

'Can you proceed against her for that?' he asked.

'It's almost impossible to prove her guilty intentions,' I said. 'All she need say is that either she borrowed the objects intending to return them, or that the old person had given her the items. Besides, some old folks don't remember their actions very clearly.'

'So it's not theft to borrow a book and not return it?'

'It's theft to borrow a book with the intention of not returning it,' I said. 'But to prosecute in such a case, we must prove that intention. That's virtually impossible. How could it be proved that a person took it with the intention of *permanently* depriving the owner of it? It's the proving of the taker's intention at the time of taking it that presents legal difficulties. Borrowing, in itself, isn't theft … '

'Could you prosecute her to frighten her off? Even if you failed to get a conviction, it might stop her antics.'

'We'd have difficulty, all our key witnesses are dead!' I smiled ruefully. 'Our prosecution department would never let it proceed. Besides, no court would convict her.'

'So what can we do?' he asked. 'I'd like to stop her, if only for the sake of the genuine benefactors.'

'I'll give the matter some thought,' I promised him. 'And I'll keep in touch.'

Over the ensuing months, I watched Miss Stirling continue to visit her old folks, and there's little doubt she was a kindly and hard-working volunteer. And then I learned that poor old Abraham Salter was dying. He was a retired schoolmaster, a bachelor with no known relatives, and he lived in a rented estate cottage at Crampton. He had cancer, I discovered, and was not expected to live beyond Christmas. And, I noticed, he was being visited regularly by Miss Stirling.

This situation had all the hallmarks of those earlier episodes, and so I decided to keep an eye on developments. I decided I must visit old Mr Salter and found a reason when there was yet another scare about bogus council workers; men were entering the homes of old folks under the pretence of checking their water supply, and they were then stealing money and other goods. I toured all the old folks on my patch, warning them about these villains. And one of the old men on my list was Mr Salter.

The nurse was with him when I arrived, and she made us a cup of tea, saying it was nice that he had a visitor. In spite of his severe illness, he was mentally alert and I had an enjoyable talk with him. Our conversation turned to books, for I saw that his room was lined with them, and it transpired that he was an authority on the Brontës, but, owing to his work, the fact he had never owned a car and now his state of health, he had never revisited the famous parsonage since seeing it as a child, nor had he joined the Brontë society. He reckoned membership would not be of benefit to him.

He pointed to a space on his shelf. 'Over there, Mr Rhea, is a scarce edition of six volumes, a complete collection of all seven novels of the Brontë sisters.'

'There are only five volumes here,' I said pointedly. 'Perhaps you are reading the sixth?'

'No, that nice Miss Stirling asked if she could borrow it – she loves the Brontës, you see. It's Charlotte's *Jane Eyre* that's missing. I let her take it – she'll return it soon, she assures me.

She does call a lot, you know. She looks after me, she's very nice.'

I saw the nurse glance at me and I knew what was going through her mind; without her saying anything, I knew she had encountered Miss Stirling's 'borrowings' before. Other patients must have mentioned it.

'Mr Salter wants to have the contents of his house sold, and the proceeds given to the Brontë society,' she told me.

'But those volumes, well, surely you'll donate those as they are?' I suggested. 'You'd not sell them.'

'Miss Stirling, who knows antiques, said the Brontë society already has a set of these, and she said she'd been in touch with them at Haworth and they'd said that cash from the sale of my collection would be of greater benefit,' he said. 'In the future, they need to extend the visitors' part of the premises at the parsonage, you see, and are keen to raise funds for building work.'

'Did she say that?' I said, my own eyes reflecting my scepticism. 'I'll check for you, shall I? If I ring them and mention your books, they'll tell me what's best – but don't tell Miss Stirling what I'm doing!'

'I think Mr Salter would appreciate that,' said the nurse. And the alert Mr Salter smiled.

The society did say that, of course, all bequests were most gratefully received and that funds for improvements to the facilities were always welcome, but that his complete set of the sisters' works was a 'must' for their library and museum. If Mr Salter would donate those books, the society would be forever grateful ... and he was invited to visit the parsonage to make the presentation.

I had great pleasure, therefore, in knocking at Miss Stirling's door one day to ask for the return of *Jane Eyre* as Mr Salter was being taken to Haworth, with his nurse, to present the entire set to the Brontë Society. If looks could have killed, I would have shrivelled and disappeared, but she did produce the volume and hand it over.

'I always intended giving it back to him,' she snapped.

'And all those other things you've borrowed from old folks,' I heard myself saying against my better judgement, and I then heard myself running through a list of the things I knew she'd borrowed. And then I added, 'And I'll be visiting the old folks to see what's missing, and the auction rooms....'

She spat at me, her tiny features a picture of hate and spite as she slammed the door in my face. Three months later, she sold her house and went to live in Scotland. But she did not arrange a sale of her own house contents. I suspect it would have been like Aladdin's Cave.

* * *

Among life's parasites is a high proportion of idle and useless siblings who sponge off their parents. One man who silently suffered the waywardness of his two sons was a shopowner called Leonard Carroll. His two sons were Raymond and Graham, Raymond being the elder by some two years. Mrs Carroll had died several years previously, before I was posted to Aidensfield, and so I never knew her.

Following her death, Mr Carroll's domestic chores were undertaken by a cleaning lady.

Leonard Carroll had opened a shop in Ashfordly just after the Second World War; it was originally a one-man business which sold household goods like pots and pans, cleaning materials and some garden equipment. Through his hard work and enterprise, the business had flourished until it had grown into the market town's only department store. Gradually, Mr Carroll had purchased the adjoining properties until his store, old fashioned though it was, sold almost everything that might be required to furnish a home or dress a family. Carpets, curtains, soft furnishing, dining suites, bedroom suites, ladies' and gents' clothes, shoes, school uniforms – all could be purchased from Carroll's.

My acquaintanceship with Mr Carroll began when I was posted to Aidensfield because we bought a lot of our furniture from his shop; he always allowed generous credit with time to pay when we were short of cash. He treated everyone like that, especially young people trying to establish their own homes, as we then were. Len Carroll was a kindly man who was liked by everyone.

Over the months, I was to learn that his sons had always taken advantage of his generosity. At school, they'd never been short of pocket money but had constantly been in trouble for disorderly behaviour in class. Raymond was something of a bully while Graham teased small boys; he did tricks like throwing their satchels away or pouring ink over their books. When these horrors left school, they drank heavily and drove fast cars.... Len found them posts within his own store, but they proved to be useless and also a liability. Two members of staff had refused to work alongside them. There was some talk of Raymond fiddling the accounts in his department. Some said Leonard had been too soft with the boys after the death of their mother; some said he'd spent too much time with the business and not enough with his sons, but whatever the reason behind their rotten behaviour, they continued to sponge off their kind-hearted father as they grew into objectionable adults.

Local knowledge, gleaned through keeping my ears and eyes open, informed me that Len had frequently paid their debts, Raymond once running up a huge bill with a local bookie and Graham owing a fortune to a garage for a succession of damaged cars and their petrol. By the time I arrived in the district, Raymond was in his late forties, unmarried but with an eye for the women, while Graham, in his early forties, had unsuccessfully tried to run his own shops. Each of his many schemes had failed because of his inefficiency and mismanagement.

Not many months after our arrival at Aidensfield, I discovered that Leonard was approaching retirement and had decided to end his active involvement with the store. He would continue to own it, however, but would appoint a manager.

When these new plans were put into operation, his two sons

rapidly found themselves no longer able to sponge from him. He made sure his own money was beyond their reach and was known to have said he intended to enjoy his few years in retirement without their parasitic demands. He openly said he had done enough for them – now they were on their own.

In the months that followed, I got to know him fairly well because he sold his large house in Ashfordly and came to live in a more modest home at Aidensfield. There he began to attend Mass at St Aiden's Catholic Church. Until that time, I did not know we shared the same faith and I was pleased when he joined the work of the parish with great enthusiasm.

He had reached sixty-five years of age by that time and we all knew he had made his will. We knew because he had stipulated that upon his death his entire estate, except for the shop, be sold and that the proceeds should go to the NSPCC. He felt that many deserving children would benefit. The shop, he said, was to be made into a trust, the trustees ensuring that it continued for the benefit of the town and its people. In the event of the shop failing to remain a viable business, then it must be sold and the proceeds donated to the NSPCC.

The two wayward sons were left entirely out of his will. He openly said they had had enough from him; they had had their opportunities, they had enjoyed his generosity and they had failed to make good use of his fatherly assistance. Now it was too late – they would not inherit his shop or his money.

It was no secret in the village that they were very hurt and angry; they were bitter and they argued with their father, saying they'd reform if he would change his will in their favour. But he had heard it all before and steadfastly refused. His mind was made up.

This information filtered to the villagers, as such information is wont to do in close communities, and we were all pleased. No one had liked the sons' treatment of their kind-hearted father and we all felt they had been justly rewarded for their past stupidity and the hurt they had inflicted on their father. But they did not give up. They began to visit him at his home, even staying for the weekend under the pretext of caring for him. He told me,

'They keep on at me to change my will in their favour, Nick, but I'll not give in, not now. I know they're my own flesh and blood, but I've given them lots of chances to make good, more chances than most lads would ever get.'

Their pressure clearly worried him and I felt pleased he was able to talk to me about his concern. Then he had a heart attack. Father Luke, the parish priest, had found him collapsed in his kitchen and had rushed him into intensive care. Len had rallied; his sons did visit him as did many villagers, including myself. In time, he was back at home, albeit under doctor's orders to take things easy.

He was a long way off seventy years of age, but the pressures of work had finally made him pay the price and he was never fully fit again. He did potter in his garden, he did visit the store once or twice a week, and he did work for the parish, making sure the grass and paths about the church were tidy, doing running repairs to the fabric and so on. But he was far less active than the Leonard Carroll we all knew. Whenever I saw him, he looked pale and under pressure. We discovered that the reason was Raymond, his eldest son.

'He never lets me alone,' Len confided in me one day. 'Always harping on about changing my will ... he says he'll reform, he'll run the store like I wanted him to ... but I can't trust him, Nick, not now ... he's made such a mess of his life, he's let me down so often. I'd far rather my money went to help some poor kids who'll appreciate it.'

'It's your decision,' I said. 'No one can advise you, Len, no one.'

'I just wish they wouldn't keep on at me, it's so bloody tiring, Nick. I'm dreading their visits now. Graham's at it as well – I think Raymond's persuaded him to nag at me.'

I did my best to console him, and was tempted to warn off the roguish sons, but knew that such family matters were really no concern of mine, however unpleasant the sons' treatment of their ailing father. Sadly, we all knew that Leonard was very ill indeed, we knew that he was dying.

He suffered further heart attacks and it wasn't long before he was confined to his bed, with a nurse calling regularly. One Sunday, after Mass, I called in to see him and was surprised to see both sons leaving, each looking happy. When I arrived at his bedside, his nurse made me a coffee and I settled down for a chat. I said I'd seen Raymond and Graham departing.

'I've altered my will,' he said with resignation. 'In their favour ... I had to, Nick, they just kept on at me ... mind, I haven't signed it yet. My solicitor's drawing it up in legal jargon, and he'll fetch it as soon as it's ready. Will you be a witness when I sign it? I've asked Father Luke to be the other witness....'

'Yes, of course, but are you sure you want to do that? To alter it in their favour?'

'Aye,' he said wearily. 'Aye, I am. I've just told the lads, I want a bit of peace now.'

The next thing I knew was that there was an urgent call for my presence at Len's bedside. I was on patrol at the time and Mary, my wife, managed to ring Divisional Headquarters who called me on the radio in the van and diverted me to Len's house. When I arrived, I saw the doctor's car, the nurse's car and those of his two sons. I hurried inside. A solicitor met me on the stairs. I recognized him as Mr Mitchell from Eltering whom I'd often encountered in court and he said,

'Mr Rhea, Mr Carroll is dying. Father Luke is with him now. He's given him the last rites. The doctor says there's no hope. I'm here with his will ... as you know, he changed it at the last minute, and the sons are here ... '

'They would be!' I said. 'Has he signed it yet?'

'No, we're waiting for you. He wanted you to be one of the two witnesses – Father Luke is the other. Father Luke specifically asked that you be here.'

'I'll do it,' I said somewhat reluctantly, for I had no wish to overtly delay things, even if it did mean the sons benefiting. That would have been against Len's last wishes and the priest knew that. I followed Mr Mitchell into the bedroom, but in those short moments, things had already happened. Len had died.

'He's dead,' Dr Archie McGee stood up as we entered. 'I'm sorry ... he just went ... '

'But he signed his will before he died,' said Raymond coldly, and no one could miss the look of triumph on his face.

Father Luke had the document in his hand and nodded. 'It was touch and go ... Raymond had to hold his hand, he moved it ... I'm sure Len was still alive when he signed ... just ... '

I could have felled Raymond there and then, forcing a dying man's hand like that ... but I could not argue because I had not been in the room at the precise moment and neither had the solicitor. But Father Luke seemed content with this bizarre turn of events.

Dr McGee closed Len's eyes. 'The precise moment of death is never easy to determine,' was all he contributed.

Whatever the precise moment of Leonard Carroll's death, his sons now had the amended will which bore their father's important signature. But it was not yet witnessed, and no one, other than the solicitor, knew the precise contents of that will. I was later to suspect that Father Luke did know something of his parishioner's deepest wishes.

'I've signed it,' said Father Luke as we assembled downstairs. 'You need not shrink from being a witness, Nick. This is his will and you know his signature.'

The solicitor handed me the document and I saw the wavy handwriting of the deceased man; I had seen his writing often enough and did recognize it as Len's work, even if it was very shaky. I looked at the priest; he knew my views on the two sharks lurking in the background, awaiting the moment their lives would be changed. But Father Luke merely smiled at me and nodded. 'Go ahead, Nick, it was Len's wish.'

'If it's his wish, I'll sign,' and so I did.

Later, I was to be very pleased that I did witness that signature and that the will had been made. Len had altered his will in his sons' favour, but not in the way they had envisaged. He had still left his shop in trust and had left the bulk of his estate to the NSPCC as he had originally decided. But he had changed his will to set aside enough money for each of the sons to be buried in church. And that was all.

Upon their deaths, their funerals would be paid for out of his estate, and when it was all over, any residue would be paid to the NSPCC....

I felt they would remember their father and their own waywardness for a long, long time.

4   The Devil Looks After His Own

Suddenly, as rare things will, it vanished.
Robert Browning (1812–89)

The sight of two women locked in mortal combat is never a pretty sight, even if the women involved are ravishingly beautiful. They fight vigorously with a lot of screaming, oath-laden catcalls and other accompanying noises: there is much swishing of handbags and hair-pulling.

A female joust can result in skulls being dented by hand-held high-heeled shoes and facial flesh being bloodied by lethal finger-nails which are like rapiers. To say that women fight like spitting, claw-wielding wild cats is a fairly accurate description, as those who have witnessed violent feminine contests can testify. After such hostilities, the contestants look like savaged rag dolls that have, quite literally, been dragged repeatedly through a hedge of vicious thorns.

A woman fighting a man is quite different – she will throw cups and saucers at him, or fling the first thing that comes into her hands even if it does contain treacle, tomato soup or wet nappies. There is generally a good deal of shrieking and other sound effects, plus the inevitable gallons of tears. If she knows the man well enough, this bout will end in oceans of salty tears and lots of urgent, healing kisses.

But the wise man will not consider the contest to be finished at that stage – one careless word can re-activate the entire war machinery.

But if there is anything worse than two women fighting in

the privacy of their own homes, it is the sight of two women doing battle in a public place. Most police officers have had to cope with female wars, often contested over garden walls or in backyards, and waged with weapons like rolling pins, clothes props and broom handles. Over the years, these bouts have provided some good entertainment, with the added bonus of some juicy gossip to follow. This is especially so if the objective of the battle was a man beloved by both parties.

But if the war-zone is a public place, then a new dimension is added and, in legal terms, the matter can become a Breach of the Peace at the very least, or involve a serious wounding offence or an affray at the most.

Like most of my colleagues, I'd sorted out a few border skirmishes between neighbours or relations but I must admit I was surprised at the sight of one particular feminine combat. It burst into action one Friday afternoon when I was on duty in Ashfordly. At the time, the market-place was full of colourful stalls as the traders shouted and sold their wares. Crowds of people, locals and holidaymakers alike, were milling around the market-place, chatting and enjoying the hot June sunshine when the double doors of the King's Head hotel burst open with a resounding crash.

It was the prelude to some great entertainment. The doors of well-designed pubs always open outwards to facilitate any necessarily swift ejection processes, and those of the King's Head then proved ideal for this purpose. As the twin doors crashed against the outer walls, there tumbled from the depths within a spitting, claw-wielding leopard and a ferocious tooth-gnashing grizzly bear. Each was endeavouring to tear the other to pieces; their warring was like a cross between bear baiting and gladitorial sparring, with a few spitting wild cats thrown in for good measure.

As the townspeople and shoppers halted to observe this circus act, they realized it wasn't a couple of wild beasts in the throes of mortal combat. It was a couple of women in fur coats. One coat was yellow and spotted like a leopard and the other was thick and brown, for all the world like the hide of a grizzly bear. And this was a summer day in June! Their wearers were fighting in a manner reminiscent of a bout between a lioness and a tigress. Even the noises and clawing were similar.

That it was a duel to the death was not in doubt. Nothing else could have produced such a rabid outcome, and so the crowds of the market-place and the people of the town wandered across to watch. Some were already striving to find the best vantage point as several from the hotel emerged to watch. Among them were more women in expensive fur coats and large, outrageously silly hats.

Here was entertainment of a very superior kind. As the pair of women, fur coats flying, legs askew, skirts above their waists and shoes cast into the far corners of the market-place, buckled down to their conflict, so the crowd began to cheer them as they would have done in bear-baiting days.

Some shouted for the leopard lady, others for the grizzly, and that was the situation which prevailed as I hove to. It was the cheers of the enthusiastic crowd that attracted my attention as I was parking my mini-van to commence a foot patrol of the market square. At first, I had no idea what was happening, thinking that the crowd's interest was in the antics of a market trader. Some stallholders were greatly entertaining, like the one who juggled with full dinner services or performed magic deeds with sharp knives and turnips. As I strolled across to the crowd, I became aware of the shrieking and screaming that was rising from the depths of the cheering masses. Here indeed was something of great interest.

'What's going on?' I asked a man standing at the edge of the crowd.

'It sounds like a bloody scrap between a couple of hundred farmyard cats,' he laughed. 'But it's two snooty women tearing themselves to pieces.'

If his assessment was correct, I had to halt the affair – brawling in a public place was definitely not the sort of thing to entertain market-day crowds, and it did seem worse because it was between two women. One did not expect this from ladies.

I pushed through the crowd, my uniform creating a buzz of

conversation from the onlookers, and when I reached the ringside, I appreciated the attraction and extent of the tournament. With the expanse of thigh, suspender, stocking-top, all revealed by rising skirts, this had the sex-appeal of women wrestling naked in mud, because these two were literally tearing the clothes off one another's backs.

The exceptions were the fur coats which seemed impervious to damage. But blouses and skirts had been ripped off, stockings shredded, shoes kicked away, handbag contents scattered....

There were a few boos and unwelcome whistles when I stepped forward to bring the proceedings to a dignified halt; I waded in, wary of course that both protagonists might turn on me with their nails, high heels and handbags. On reflection, I think I arrived just as each was realizing they were tiring rapidly, that no outright winner was likely and that they were making themselves look ridiculous. And it would be a costly bout so far as replacement clothes were concerned.

I shouted to them, demanding that they halt their battle, but at first their shrieks drowned my voice and so I had to push into the scrimmage and seize each by the collar of her fur coat. There wasn't much else left to grab at that stage, but I held them apart at arm's length. Each was now six feet from the other with me in between.

For a few brief moments, their arms flailed, their feet kicked and their voices rose to a pitch of high excitement, but all to no avail. They were now fighting thin air. It was a technique we used to separate fighting dogs. I simply held them apart until they had calmed down.

They were a sorry sight, their smart hair-styles gone, their make-up ruined, tears and mascara running down their cheeks, their feet bare and even bleeding, their reputations gone, and their fine clothes in tatters. It had been a considerable affray, but now, as I held them apart wondering what to do with them, both began to weep. The gross embarrassment of those public moments began to eat into their silly brains.

I decided to take them into the hotel whence they had emerged, albeit keeping them firmly apart. By now, the crowd was silent, wondering firstly what had started the rumpus and, secondly, what I was going to do about it. Those were my thoughts too. I decided the onlookers would never know the answer to either question, hence my decision to take the aggressors indoors. As I propelled the female gladiators inside, I saw the hotel manager hovering in the background looking decidedly worried, but he did step forward to close the door against the inquisitive crowd, some of whom were on the verge of following the drama to its lawful conclusion.

Inside the hotel's foyer, I released my grip on the furry collars, but stood between the two women.

Each was in her mid-forties and each looking decidedly humble by this time.

'Well,' I said, wondering if I sounded like a schoolmaster lecturing his erring pupils. 'What was all that about?'

Neither of them spoke. Each stood with her head hung low, in half-attire, as if the awful shame of the past few minutes had suddenly dawned. The manager, a smooth-haired man called David Sanderson, stepped forward.

'It was about an umbrella,' he said quietly.

'An umbrella?' I asked in disbelief.

'It had been left here, last month in fact. These ladies are members of the Ashfordly Ladies' Luncheon Club, you see. They love to parade in their fur coats and expensive hats … well, one of them left an umbrella behind after the last meeting.'

He paused as if to imply that the brolly was a Very Important Thing, then continued, 'Today, when I showed it to the ladies, this lady,' and he indicated the one in the leopard-skin coat, 'said it was hers. She thanked me and was walking out with it … '

'It's not Rebecca's, it's mine.' the one in the grizzly-bear coat now came to life. 'I said it was mine all along … I left it behind last time I came … it is mine, I keep telling her that.'

'It's not, you silly bitch, it's mine,' spat her foe. 'I'd know it anywhere, it's mine … '

'Hold on,' I shouted, stepping between them again lest battle be resumed, 'We're not going to suffer another fight, so just keep quiet, both of you. I've never seen such unruly behaviour from anyone, let alone women who pretend to be quality examples of their sex. You fight like alley cats instead of acting like the sophisticated women you pretend to be…. So, Mr Sanderson, where is the brolly now?'

'Mrs Fenner took it out with her … '

'And she snatched it from me … '

'No I didn't, I just wanted to look at it … '

I shouted at them again in my schoolmaster's voice, and said, 'Well, if neither of you have got it, then it's still outside, so it seems. After all this commotion, you've dropped it, one or other of you. And your shoes are still out there, as well as things from your handbags and bits of clothing … ' They looked at themselves, now horrified.

'I'll send someone out to collect their belongings,' offered Sanderson, and I said it was a great idea. The women, chaperoned by Sanderson and I, then adjourned to a more private place, a small ante-room away from the stares of hotel staff and residents. The two warring women sat with their backs to each other as Mr Sanderson and I waited for the residue of their cannonade to be brought in.

'I hope this disgraceful display does not detract from the high reputation of the hotel,' Sanderson said. 'This is most certainly not the sort of behaviour one expects … '

'It's all her fault,' hissed Mrs Fenner.

'It's not mine, it's yours,' shrieked the other, whose name I later learned was Mrs Porter.

'Quiet, the pair of you,' said I.

Sanderson went on, 'I must really take a long hard look at the luncheon club's future with us. I thought they were ladies – they call themselves ladies, but they behave like alley cats…. '

We were denied any more of his ramblings when a waitress from the hotel's dining room staff entered bearing shoes, handbags and other assorted belongings which had been gathered from the battlefield outside.

'Has the crowd gone?' I asked her.

'Yes, Mr Rhea, they've all gone,' she smiled.

'Thanks for searching for all these things,' I smiled. 'Did you find the missing umbrella?'

'No,' she said. 'I searched everywhere, it's gone. I think someone's stolen it,' she added.

And so they had. I went out and made another very thorough search, even looking under parked cars, into the branches of trees and along the patch of garden in front of the hotel, but it had gone. Now they would never know who was the true owner, but because I did not know who owned it, I could not record it as a crime. After all, who was the loser?

Sanderson and I talked to the two warriors but neither would admit being at fault, nor would they agree about ownership of the missing brolly. From my own point of view, the theft of the umbrella had been fortuitous. I'm sure that if we had recovered it, the dispute would have continued. Now, they had nothing to fight about and I said that I would take no action against them. If either wished to claim the other had assaulted her, then the remedy was to take out a private summons. I explained this could be done by contacting a solicitor. I knew that the police would not wish to become involved, and I suggested that any claims for damage to clothing should be sorted out between them. This had a calming effect and, quite surprisingly, the two women suddenly turned and clung to one another, sobbing their sorrows into the thick fur of their respective coats before going to the ladies' room to repair some of the damage.

I did hear later that both had resigned from the luncheon club, but I never did find out who really owned the disputed umbrella. But why did they fight with such determination over something as trivial and replaceable as an umbrella? I did wonder if there was another aspect to the story, whether, for example, the husband of one was illicitly seeing the other. But I did not pursue the matter.

Due to their high-profile fight, however, the luncheon club had become a laughing stock, the townspeople chuckling for many months over that drama.

They made fun of the women and their ridiculous behaviour in trying to outshine each other with their expensive and outlandish hats, fur coats, gloves and shoes. Discerning ladies were suddenly quite embarrassed to be associated with it.

The umbrella story became part of the folklore of Ashfordly, and today the missing object is probably hanging upon someone's coat hook. Perhaps it was removed by the true owner? But where did it go? And what was so special about that umbrella? The mystery remains.

★ ★ ★

Umbrella owners will know that objects of that size can easily disappear without trace, even within one's own home, but an infinitely more puzzling event involved the disappearance of something considerably larger. And, like that umbrella, the mystery remains.

I was on patrol one winter's night, working a late turn, i.e. from 2 p.m. until 10 p.m., when the puzzle developed. That tour of duty promised to be pleasant because my beat was quiet and I had no pressing commitments. I could check on vulnerable premises, visit a few friendly farmers and cottagers, make inquiries about any outstanding crimes and generally perform useful public relations duties by visiting pubs, popping into shops and other places open to the public. I'd show my uniform where it mattered; I'd visit old folk who were alone or worried and generally reappraise the welfare of those at risk.

Such work is an important part of the rural bobby's duty; consequently, leisurely patrols of this kind provided an opportunity to maintain vital contact with a wide range of people.

The afternoon passed without incident and I did fulfil many of my plans. By the time I returned home for my meal break, from 5.45 p.m. until 6.30 p.m., darkness had fallen and freezing fog was threatened. When I left the house, however, the sky was clear with the stars twinkling in the blackness above, but the air contained that distinctive hint of an imminent hard frost. I was cosy in my official van with the heating system working at peak level but was determined not to be lulled into any false sense of security, because there was a threat of ice on the roads. The forecast warned of a severe frost later that night and said it would persist for several days. The council's gritting lorries had been out earlier in the evening to spread salt along the roads and I decided I would park my van and walk where possible.

I would undertake the main part of my evening patrol on foot, making calls in Aidensfield, Elsinby, Ploatby and Crampton before knocking off at 10 p.m. There was no point in risking a motor accident on the icy roads, although I did need the van to travel between the villages.

It would be shortly after 8.30 p.m. when I received a radio call from the Control Room.

It seemed that a man from Crampton, Mr Geoffrey Dixon, who worked for a petrol supplier, had been walking his dog between Crampton and Thackerston a few minutes earlier when he had discovered a serious traffic accident. It had happened at the foot of Oak Lea Bank just outside Crampton. A small car appeared to have collided with a horse; the car was on its side in the ditch while the horse was lying injured at the scene; the car driver was not with his car and appeared to have wandered off, probably suffering from concussion. His car, it seemed from the report, was badly damaged. Mr Dixon had rushed to the nearest house from where he had telephoned. I was directed to the scene, and Control reminded me to drive carefully because of the ice. It seemed that the accident had occurred on a very slippery road surface. A vet had been called too, but the horse had no rider with it.

I knew the hill in question. It was steep and the downward slope terminated in a sweeping corner to the left; drivers often experienced trouble negotiating it and in winter it was made worse because water oozed from the fields above and ran across the highway. In severe conditions, it froze to produce a very slippery and sloping surface. I had no doubt that this was the cause of the accident. It would take me ten minutes to arrive at the scene and I gave that ETA (estimated time of arrival) to Control; they did say that owing to the probability that the driver had wandered off in an apparent concussed state, an ambulance had been called.

What looked like concussion could sometimes conceal a more serious internal injury.

Off I went to deal with the accident, driving very carefully through our narrow lanes with the stars twinkling above. My route took me through Thackerston and thus to Oak Lea Bank from its lower end. I parked the van on a wide grass verge some distance from the foot of the hill, took a powerful torch from the van and walked to the notorious corner.

But there was nothing to be seen. I saw the anticipated patch of thick ice which spread across the road, but there was no sign of an injured horse or a damaged car. The beam from my torch played across the road ahead of me and then, in the ditch just below the corner, I found evidence of the car's recent presence. There was damage to the hedge and the fence behind it, with some broken headlamp glass and red light glass upon the frozen grass and the inevitable twisted pieces of chrome strip. Chrome strips always seemed to fall off accident-damaged cars. These bits had come from a Ford Anglia. I searched everywhere along that roadside and even ventured into the adjoining fields, thinking the impetus of the car might have propelled it across one of the hawthorn hedges. But there was no damage to any of the hedges and the car was nowhere to be seen. Neither was the horse. I spent some considerable time in the darkness, checking and re-checking in my search, but the scene was deserted.

I walked the entire length of that hill with my torch, examining the ditches, gates, hedge-bottoms and all places that either a horse or a car might be concealed. But I found nothing, nor did I find the concussed driver. As I hunted, the ambulance arrived and I explained the situation to the driver; then a vet from Harrowby, a Mr Marriott, turned up to attend the horse.

Together, using the headlights of our vehicles and with torches blazing, we undertook another search of every inch of that hill and its verges, but found neither horse, car, nor man. We did, however, discover a large spot of fresh blood in the road and guessed it had come from the horse. We also found further fragments of smashed glass in the centre of the road and I noticed some piles of mud, good indications of the precise location of a collision. In a collision which involves a motor vehicle, such piles of mud invariably fall from the undersides to identify the point of impact.

'So what do you suggest, constable?' asked the vet in his light Scots accent.

'First, I'll check with Control,' I said. 'They might have given me the wrong location.'

I called them on my radio and they confirmed the location. According to them, we were all standing precisely at the scene of the reported accident.

'So what next?' persisted the vet.

'I need to have a word with Mr Dixon, the man who reported it. He didn't ring me, he rang our Control Room,' I explained. 'They diverted me here. He lives in Crampton, I know his house. I can be there and back in two minutes – I'll ask him to come and show us where it happened.'

The vet looked at the ambulance driver and both agreed to wait for those extra minutes, just in case we had been directed to the wrong place. If we had, then their skills may be needed elsewhere. I hurried off to Geoff Dixon's cottage in my van and he answered the door.

'It's about the accident you reported, Geoff,' I began.

'It's at the bottom of Oak Lea Bank, Mr Rhea. I rang your headquarters.'

'Yes, but there's nothing there. I've got a vet and an ambulance down there, as well as myself, and we're all looking for casualties – but there's nothing. Can you come and show us exactly where it happened?'

'Sure, I'll get my coat.'

He directed me to the place I'd already visited and stood in the road, baffled. We all stood and looked at him.

'It was definitely here,' he pointed to the mess in the hedge. 'The car was there, on its side, and it was pretty badly damaged … but there was nobody with it. And the horse was lying down there, on that wide bit of verge. There was blood on its flank – it looked like a bad stomach wound and it was panting heavily, but alive…. I ran to call the police.'

'I got the call at 8.30 p.m.,' I said, looking at my watch. It was now ten minutes past nine. We'd spent the interim searching.

'It would take me a good five minutes to run and make the call, but the accident might have happened some time before I arrived. Maybe the man in the car rang from somewhere, or a pal was with him or something….'

'So it might have occurred an hour ago?' I said, thinking that that left sufficient time for someone to come and clear away the damaged car and remove the horse. With Dixon helping us, we made another complete search of the neighbouring fields and road verges, but found nothing. I thanked the vet and the ambulance for coming all this way on icy roads for nothing, but said I had no idea where the casualties had gone.

I took Geoff Dixon home and he invited me in for a cup of coffee; I went over his experience once again, getting a detailed description of the car and the horse, just to satisfy myself that the incident *had* occurred, but of that, there was no doubt.

Even today, I do not know what happened to that car driver or his Ford Anglia car, nor do I know what happened to the injured horse. I am convinced that Dixon had not imagined the accident – the evidence at the scene confirmed his experience. But of the casualties? They vanished on that frosty night in January.

*   *   *

Another curious instance of disappearing property occurred

when someone allegedly stole sheep from Frank Huggett. Frank ran a huge flock on the open moors above Gelderslack, his black-faced ewes living almost wild upon those bleak and heathery heights. They had no fences to keep them in and they spread themselves across a spacious area of heather and bracken, fending for themselves for most of the year. Then, every three months or so, Frank would ride the range upon his horse, accompanied by his team of three dogs, and he would bring his flock down to the lower reaches for clipping or for counting or dipping when required.

But these sheep did not stray from their pastures because they were heeafed, pronounced hee-affed. This curious dialect word comes from *heaf* meaning home, and in this case it means that the sheep know their own territory and will remain there without the need for fences. Whole flocks are heeafed and the local name for these sheep is therefore heeafed yows (heafed ewes).

Frank claimed he could recognize every one of his ewes, even though all were black-faced with horns, and had the distinctive black legs. To anyone else, they were like peas in the proverbial pod, except that there were hundreds of them. But Frank knew their individual faces as a head teacher knows the faces of all the school's pupils; he could remember which ewe had had twins or triplets, which had been ill or missing in the counting sessions and which needed the greatest care.

That Frank loved his sheep was never in doubt. Some said he was sheep-fond or sheep-daft, meaning he thought of nothing else, just as some Yorkshire lasses are known as lad-fond. Certainly, every minute of Frank's life, whether working or at leisure, was dominated by his flocks, and it was equally well known that he was regarded as an expert on moorland sheep and was a leading member of the Black-faced Sheep Breeders' Association.

He judged at shows and was often called by his friends to give advice, and yet his formal education had been virtually nil. He'd left the village school at fourteen to follow his father into moorland sheep-farming and had been willing both to work hard and to learn from his highly experienced father. With his father and mother long dead, Frank and his wife did keep some other animals – goats could be seen about his farm buildings and his wife bred geese, ducks and poultry. Frank even reckoned to be able to identify every hen on the premises.

* * *

So far as his sheep were concerned, people would often put Frank to the test, asking him to identify a particular ewe and to provide its history. And he would oblige. He'd say,

'Yon awd lass had triplets two year back, and she's been wi' me nigh on fower year. Ah gat her at Eltering Mart. Ah calls her Elsie Seven and she's allus given a good fleece, thick and full. She's been a good lamber an' all, and Ah reckon there's a year or two in her yet. She's a grand awd lass is yon.'

The name of Elsie Seven intrigued me. He did give names to most of his ewes, but because he had such a huge flock he ran out of names. Thus, several sheep bore the same female Christian name, with a numeral for their surname. He would often point out a sheep in the distance, saying she was Kate Three, the daughter of Mary Nine and that she'd had three lambs in three years, the other two being Nancy Two and Brenda Eight. It was a joy to hear him counting his sheep, shouting at Joan Eleven to 'git oot o' t'rooad' or Lily One to 'sharpen thisell and git between yon fences'.

Frank's individual system of identification was, of course, in addition to the standard one which is used for moorland sheep. Because several farmers run their flocks on the open moors, the animals must be identified as belonging to a particular person. Quite often, the sheep of one farmer mingle with those of another and confusion would occur without a simple and highly visible identification method. That method involves the use of coloured dye; thus moorland sheep will have splashes of red, green or blue dye upon their wool. One farmer might mark all members of his flock with a red left foreshoulder; another might use a green rump or another a blue right hand quarter. I have heard townspeople cry with alarm at seeing a sheep with a bright red patch on its belly wool – they thought it had been injured, but it was just the owner's mark.

Tups are also marked with dye under their bellies before they embark upon fatherhood. As they serve each ewe, so they leave behind a brightly coloured patch on the ewe's rump – red is a favourite colour – and so the farmer knows which of his ewes have or have not been charmed into future motherhood by the busy tup. Ear clipping is another means of identification, with members of each flock having distinctive marks upon their ears.

But in Frank Huggett's distinctive method of naming his sheep, who could prove him wrong? If he made such claims about knowledge of his animals, how could anyone prove otherwise? Not that anyone would – they all trusted him and I had no reason to doubt his expertise. If he said he knew every single one of his sheep by their first names, then neither I nor anyone else doubted him. He was a fine man, a solid, likeable moorland farmer who stood no nonsense from anyone. Now approaching fifty-five, he was a thick-set character with a surprisingly pink complexion beneath his head of wavy greying hair. Bright blue eyes gave him a baby-faced look, and he was always particular about his appearance, never going unshaven and always having neat haircuts.

You'd rarely find him indoors; whenever I called, morning, noon or night, Frank would be somewhere on the moors with his dogs and shepherd's crook, checking his flock for one thing or another. On one occasion, he went out in blizzard conditions, to take a supply of hay to some of his flock who had been marooned on the windswept heights. He learned they had found shelter in an old barn on the moors high above his farmhouse.

Nonetheless, he went out in appalling conditions to see to them and to take them food. He reckoned the safety of his sheep was more important than sitting cosily beside his blazing kitchen fire. It's not surprising that his friends called

him Awd Moorender. Moorender is a slightly derogatory term
for a rough character who lives on the moors and who is not
sophisticated like townspeople. Indeed, lots of townies refer to
country folk of this region (like me!) as moorenders, the
implication being that moorenders are simpletons.

The word is also used for rough sheep or even horses that
live on these heights. If a man had a tired, shaggy old horse,
people would describe it as a moorender. In spite of this, I'd
say that Frank was a moorender, but he was by no means a
simpleton. His wife never complained of his devotion to the
sheep, for she had produced three lovely children, now in
their twenties, and occupied herself with village organizations
like the WI and the PCC of the small parish church.

I do not know if the sheep responded to the dedication that
Frank lavished upon them – they are rather stupid animals,
unlike dogs who will respond to a master's love and trust. But
Frank seemed to think that they knew him and loved him, and
that they welcomed his constant care and affection. Perhaps
they did. That thought made him very happy and contented.

It was therefore a most hurtful experience when he
discovered that two of his flock had been stolen.

For Frank, it was tantamount to someone kidnapping his
child, and the matter clearly upset him. He was upset rather
than angry. I learned of this crime through a telephone call.

'Somebody's ta'en a pair of my sheep, Mr Rhea,' he told me
shortly after eight one morning. 'Can thoo come and see me?'

I said I'd be there within twenty minutes. As I drove across
the moor, I wondered if they had really been stolen. Sheep did
go astray; some got stuck in ditches and others wandered into
distant corners of their heeaf. Some were run down by
motorists and some simply died in isolation. Few farmers
could supervise every single inch of the huge open area of
countryside in which their flocks lived and so we had to treat
every case of reported theft with just a hint of caution.
Nonetheless, sheep rustling did occur. Thieves armed with
.22 rifles would shoot the animals which grazed near the
roadside. The carcasses were immediately skinned on the spot

and placed in the rear of a van, the discarded skins being thrown far into the heather. Thus, if we caught a thief in possession of a carcass, it was impossible to prove where it had come from, and virtually impossible to locate the discarded skin and fleece. Such slaughtered carcasses were sold to butchers in the surrounding towns. Was this the fate of Frank's animals?

When I interviewed Frank in his cosy kitchen, enjoying the inevitable 'lowance and huge mug of tea, I had to cast doubt upon his theft theory.

I did so by asking whether the sheep could be stuck in a ditch, whether they might have wandered into a neighbour's heeaf, whether they had simply died or whether they were victims of a road accident. But he was adamant.

'Last night, t'pair on 'em was up near Holm Intak, doon bi t'stream. Ah knows 'em, Mr Rhea, them two's been pals since they were lambs. Maud Seven and Doris Twelve, they go ivverywhere together them two, cousins they are. You'll nivver see yan withoot t'other, so if yan had been trapped or run over, t'other would be standing by, bleating for me to come and do summat. They've both gone, Mr Rhea, and in my book, that means somebody's pinched 'em.'

I had no option but to accept his word. I could not visit the scene of the crime because they might have been stolen from anywhere within thousands of acres, but after convincing myself that Frank was correct, I decided to 'crime' the report of the missing sheep. That meant it was officially recorded as a crime and I was sure Frank would then be able to claim from his insurance if his animals were not recovered alive.

'Frank,' I said, 'you realize we stand very little chance of recovering your sheep? If the thieves have clipped off your dye marks, we'll never prove they are yours even if we catch the thief.... To be brutally honest, I think they'll probably be lamb chops by now, on sale in some butcher's shop in Middlesbrough or Sunderland. But I'll circulate the theft to all our officers and we will make wide inquiries.'

'Ah know there's nowt much you fellers can do, but

t'insurance says we must report thefts to you blokes. But Ah's off to Eltering Mart this morning, Mr Rhea, and if them sheep o' mine are there, Ah'll recognize 'em even if t'markings have been shaven off. If their faces are there, Ah'll know 'em!'

'If you do see them, call us,' I cautioned him. 'Don't take the law into your own hands!'

On my return journey to Aidensfield, I popped into the police office at Ashfordly to record the crime and decided to spend a few moments in that office, typing up my initial crime report. It took me about an hour, and as I was finishing it off, the telephone rang. It was Frank Huggett.

'Ah rang your house, but your missus said you'd likely be there,' he began. 'Ah've found them sheep, Mr Rhea, like Ah said. Maud Seven and Doris Twelve. At Eltering Mart. In a pen. T'licence bobby 'as isolated 'em; t'pen belongs to awd Ernie Stubbs. Thoo knaws as well as me that we've suspected 'im for years. 'E's pinched more sheep that Ah've had hot dinners, and nut once 'as 'e been caught. Well, we've got him red-handed, Mr Rhea, you'll be pleased to know.'

'Where are you ringing from?' I asked.

'T'mart office,' he said.

'I'll come straight away,' I told him. 'Tell the Mart PC I'm on my way and ask him to keep Ernie Stubbs and the sheep there.'

'Right ho, Mr Rhea.'

At every cattle mart, there used to be a constable on duty and his task was to issue pig licences as well as to keep a general eye on the proceedings. That system operated in my time as a village constable and it was fortunate that a constable was there on this occasion. When I arrived twenty-five minutes later, I went to the office and found PC John Rogers of Eltering Police. He had isolated the suspect animals and had also detained Ernie Stubbs; he was now in Eltering Police Station cells, under arrest for suspected theft. 'I had to lift him on suspicion,' said PC Rogers to me. 'Mind, he says he didn't steal those sheep, says he's never been near Frank Huggett's spot.'

'He would say that, wouldn't he?' I smiled.

'But, Nick, you can't prove those are Mr Huggett's sheep, can you? One sheep looks just like any other ... '

'Ah know my sheep,' said Frank stolidly. 'Them's mine, Mr Rogers, there's neea doubt aboot it.'

'Let's have a look at them,' I suggested.

The tiny pen contained two timid looking sheep, both black-faced ewes with horns and black legs, but neither bearing any ear clipping marks or dyed wool. To my inexpert eye, they looked like identical twins; I could see no difference in them.

'He's clipped my colour off,' said Frank, touching each animal on its shoulder to indicate the site of the missing dye. 'Thoo knows, Mr Rhea, Ah's a red right shoulder man. Thoo can see where t'fleece 'as been trimmed.'

He was right. The wool around that shoulder had been recently cut short, but whether a court would accept that as evidence of the removal of identifying marks and thus an indication of theft, remained to be seen.

'But these sheep don't respond to you,' said PC Rogers to Frank.

'They do!' he cried. 'They know me, but sheep are not daft, Mr Rogers, they don't show emotion like dogs, they don't make a fuss.... Them two's my ewes, mak neea mistake.'

'Frank is an expert on moorland sheep,' I informed Rogers. 'I'm sure that if he gave evidence in court, as an expert witness, it would be treated with great respect.'

Thus we were faced with something of a dilemma, for I doubted whether our own prosecution department would accept Frank's opinion that these were indeed his animals. After all, anyone could claim ownership of anything if absolute proof became an unnecessary prerequisite. But I did believe Frank and felt that the decision should rest with a court. As Frank had said, we had long suspected Stubbs of sheep stealing; indeed, we were positive he was a regular thief but we had never been able to prove a single case against him. We'd never caught him in possession of the stolen animals.

To cut a long story short, Stubbs was charged with theft of

Frank's two ewes and, in court, steadfastly denied any responsibility for that crime.

He refused to reveal from where he had obtained the two ewes in question and denied clipping off the red identification mark. The magistrates listened to Frank's simple explanation of his reputed ability to identify every animal in his flock of over eight hundred, and the court accepted his status as an expert on moorland sheep. I felt sure the court would decide that there was reasonable doubt about Stubb's guilt and that they would acquit him of theft, but as one of the magistrates was himself a moorland farmer, I reckon the bench knew of Ernie Stubb's reputation and of Frank's legendary skill. So he was found guilty and fined £50.

About a month later, I called at Frank's lonely farm for my quarterly visit to sign his stock register and I was invited to join him and his wife for 'lowance. I mentioned that we'd had no subsequent reports of sheep stealing since Stubbs's conviction and thanked Frank for his efforts in convicting him.

'Somebody 'ad to sort him out, Mr Rhea.' A knowing smile flickered across his pink face. ' 'E's been at it for years without getting caught.'

'But now he's been convicted of sheep stealing, the local markets will be less keen to take stuff from him?'

'Aye,' beamed Frank. ' 'E'll not pinch sheep unless 'e can sell 'em, and 'e can't sell 'em if nobody'll take 'em off 'is 'ands. Ah reckon we fettled him good and proper, Mr Rhea.'

'It still baffles me how you can tell one sheep from another, Frank,' I laughed.

'He can't,' commented his wife. 'He makes it all up, it's his party trick!'

'But two o' my ewes were missing ewes and Ah've get two back. If Ah say they're mine, then mine they are!' grinned Frank. 'And we've stopped Stubbs. Moorenders aren't so daft after all, are they, Mr Rhea?'

'Fortunately, no!' I heard myself saying. 'And I can record a crime as being detected.' It was all that I, as another moorender, could think of adding.

5   Fellowship and Social Assembly

Their judgement is a mere lottery
John Dryden (1631–1700)

The legal name for tombola or a raffle is a *lottery* and in my time as village constable at Aidensfield there were only four types of lottery, other than premium bonds, which were legal in this country. Every other lottery was unlawful.

The definition of a lottery is 'a distribution of prizes by lot or chance', the important element being that there should be no skill involved. A lottery is won by sheer chance or good fortune, hence the need for legal control.

To conform to the then prevailing law, there were sets of rules to govern each of the four legal types of lottery. One which rarely featured in police work was the lottery of an art union. Members of an art union drew lots, the winners being allowed to retain certain works of art for a specified period.

The other three types of lottery were more widespread i.e.:

(1) *Small lotteries* which were incidental to popular entertainments like jumble sales, dinners, dances and sporting events. Tickets for those were sold and drawn on the premises during the event and it was a rule (often broken) that no cash prizes could be given. The prizes were generally things like boxes of chocolates, groceries, toiletries and similar gifts.

(2) *Private lotteries* which were restricted to members of a

society, say a football supporters' club. In this case, all the proceeds, less expenses, had to be donated to the charity and certain rules had to be followed.

(3) *Registered lotteries*. These had to be registered with the local authority and organized for charitable purposes, but the prizes could be larger, like holidays overseas or TV sets, provided the value of each prize (at that time) did not exceed £100. Tickets for these lotteries could be sold before or during the event, and sold off the premises. Each ticket had to contain the name of the charity, the promoter of the raffle and the cost of each ticket (which should not exceed one shilling – 5p).

From time to time, organizations wanted to stage a massive raffle with a huge prize like a motor car, but the trick was to remove the competition from the status of a lottery. This could be done by incorporating some act of skill, like estimating the number of peas in a jam jar, estimating how many yards a car could be driven on one gallon of petrol, estimating the weight of a cake or a baby, or calculating the time the pointers of a clock would stop if it wasn't wound up. All kinds of skilful deeds were introduced to remove such contests from the lottery laws. Lots of organizations ran these so-called prize competitions instead of raffles, but the good old village raffle continued to flourish in spite of any newfangled ideas.

At most village raffles, numbered cloakroom tickets in various colours were sold to people at social functions, but the rules of these small lotteries were generally ignored or not even considered. Little old ladies cheerfully broke the law by organizing raffles for cash prizes or selling the tickets around the village before the event took place. It would not surprise me if committees continue to break the law concerning small lotteries, but who complains? And who knows what those laws are? Who, apart from the village constable, was then familiar with the Betting, Gaming and Lotteries Act of 1963?

A village constable had to close his eyes to some breaches of that statute, such as those occasions where, for example, a teddy bear was raffled by tickets sold in the village shop. As this was not 'incidental to an entertainment' like a dinner, dance, social event or sporting fixture, it was an unlawful lottery. It might be argued by some that shopping was 'entertainment', but it is doubtful whether the courts would agree with that interpretation. But as the proceeds were going to charity, who would complain?

If, on the other hand, some wily character was making money for himself by this means, then, of course, we would step in and prosecute. It's a matter of applying the law with common sense, because to rigidly enforce every rule and regulation, as some politicians demand, would result in a police state.

In such cases, suitable advice was often given to the unwitting law-breakers. I did hear of some strange raffles – one man who worked in a large factory always raffled his wage packets and made more from that than he did from his wages. As the dastardly deed was not on my patch, I was not concerned with that enterprising illegality. Another man, again not on my beat, decided to raffle his house when it was on the market for a long time, but I don't think it was a successful venture. He failed to sell enough tickets to cover the value of his property.

To give most of the village raffle organizers due credit, they did come to me for advice when they were about to embark upon a new project. In many cases, I was able to help, sometimes suggesting that an act of skill be incorporated to provide greater appeal, especially when it was for a worthwhile cause. And, as Aidensfield's chief raffle consultant, I was invariably asked to buy tickets, but my record of wins was abysmal. Some people always win and some never do; I was in the latter category, while a friend who worked in a turkey factory always won several turkeys at Christmas, and a local publican always won bottles of whisky.

It was during my involvement with raffles in Aidensfield and the surrounding villages that I noticed a curious phenomenon. The strangeness did not make itself immediately apparent, but materialized only after I'd attended about a dozen social events in various village halls.

I noticed that every raffle prize list contained a tin of sardines. I guessed the donor was a local grocer. The local licensees always gave bottles of whisky or gin, the butchers gave hams or pheasants, the garages gave cans of oil or vouchers for free petrol, the hairdressers gave vouchers for free hair-styling and local restaurants offered free meals for two in cosy candlelit places. As the village constable, there was little I could offer by way of a professional prize – I could hardly offer fine-free vouchers for speeding or the chance to drink after hours without being caught – and so I tried to buy something different for each raffle, like an ornament, perfume, book, picture and so forth. With about a dozen villages and hamlets on my patch, it was an expensive indulgence because there was usually a raffle somewhere every month, either for the WI, a football or cricket club, gardening club, playgroup and one or other of the churches, but never the chapels.

Mary and I tried to socialize at these events as often as we could, our appearances being heavily dependent upon baby-sitters and my odd working-hours, but it did become clear that the villagers keenly supported one another's raffles. They attended each other's WI meetings, whist drives, dances and so on. It was very heart-warming to see them supporting one another.

It was during these events that I came to notice that whenever a tin of sardines was won in the raffle, there was an almighty cheer from the audience. It was surely because no one really wanted to win it!

While not wishing to show my curiosity or ignorance about it, and never wanting to appear silly by asking why everyone cheered the tin of sardines, it was then that I realized that almost every local raffle had a tin of sardines as a prize. There were one or two exceptions, usually when two events occurred simultaneously in different villages. I began to wonder about the identity of the supplier – which benefactor had all those tins to spare, I wondered? Where were they coming from? Was there something odd going on? Something that I ought to be familiar with? That sardine-cheering was a puzzle.

Then the inevitable happened. Mary and I attended a dance in aid of church funds and, sure enough, raffle tickets were on sale. I bought some and resigned myself to the fact that I would never win. I never did – I regarded that investment as a donation to church funds.

It is not difficult, therefore, to imagine my surprise when I found I had a winning ticket, the last one of that evening – and that my prize was a tin of sardines. As I strode forward to claim it, there was an almighty cheer. From past experience, I had expected the cheer, but as I bore the small tin triumphantly back to my seat, Mary asked,

'Why did they cheer like that?'

I told her about the custom I'd witnessed at other events but added, 'But I don't really know why they do it – it's just that every time a tin of sardines is won, everybody cheers.'

'There must be a reason,' she said.

'It's like dropping a plate or a cup in a works canteen – everybody cheers when that happens!' I told her.

Without really inspecting the tin, I slipped it into my jacket pocket and joined the dancing. It was a pleasant evening and we enjoyed it, but as the dance was drawing to a close, the organizer, Charles Thackray, approached me.

'I was glad you and Mrs Rhea could join us socially,' he said. 'I hope we'll see you again.'

'We've enjoyed it.' I meant every word. 'If my duties allow, and we can find a baby-sitter, we'll come again.'

'And you've no more worries about what to give as the next raffle prize,' he laughed.

'The sardines?' I realized what he was talking about and knew it was the perfect time to ask about the cheering custom. 'Tell me, Mr Thackray, why does everyone cheer when tins of sardines are won?'

'You don't know?' he sounded surprised.

'Well, to be honest, no I don't.'

'I'll warn you,' he chuckled. 'Don't try to open that tin and don't eat the contents!'

I took it out of my pocket and looked at it.

Then I realized that the design of the label was ancient – it was like those tins of sardines I'd seen when I was a child – and apart from that, the label and indeed the tin looked worn and shabby. It was an extremely old tin of extremely old sardines.

'That tin's more than thirty years old,' he laughed. 'It's been going around these villages since before the war. It's always given as a raffle prize, Mr Rhea – whoever wins it gives it back as a prize. It's not for opening, you see, it's for winning in raffles.'

'You mean this is the same tin I've seen at all those raffles?'

'Aye, that's why they all cheer. So when you're asked to give a prize next time, you give it back.'

'Thanks for warning me!' I said. 'We might have opened it.... '

'You'd have had to buy a new tin,' he said. 'We always have a tin of sardines at all our raffles. It's a good prize, you know, it saves you having to find a prize for the next raffle!'

As I looked at it, I wondered how many more of those raffle prizes were never opened, being recycled in village raffles. It was less than a week later when Mrs Allen stopped me in Elsinby and asked,

'It's our WI raffle next month, Mr Rhea. I wondered if you might give a prize – I hear you've got the tin of sardines?'

'I'll fetch it along,' I promised her.

And until I left the area, that tin of sardines was still being won in local raffles.

* * *

Among the 'entertainments' at which raffles were held was the village whist drive, a most serious affair. Every week, on whist night, the village hall was prepared with green-baize card tables in readiness for this major social event. A supper was arranged and people from the surrounding area would arrive to compete with one another. There was immense honour in winning first prize. The prize itself, something like a brace of pheasants or a box of groceries, was secondary to the pride and honour in actually beating all-comers in this most honourable of contests. There was sometimes a First Man prize and a First Woman prize, and occasionally, if the organizer had a sense of humour, a wooden spoon for the lowest scorer. As opening time arrived, men, women and children, all gripped with the fever of winning, arrived early to ensure a good seat at their lucky starting table.

Almost every village had its own whist drives, their popularity being legendary. The moors were rich with stories of this card game, with certain players never losing, others always winning when hearts were shinners (trumps), some being lucky at full moon or some only when there was an 'r' in the month.

Stories would circulate far and wide about Awd Isaac who never had an ace in his hand but won nonetheless, of Awd Mrs Blenkin who thought spades were omens of death and always lost when she got the ace, and of Awd Jack Harrison whose winning streak lasted over five years until somebody trumped his king of diamonds with the two of clubs. He was ill for months afterwards, blaming himself for not correctly reading the other's hand.

Whist drives were often varied to give added spice to the proceedings. For example, there would be military whist drives in which the players formed teams which represented nations. Each team was allocated a little flag and thus nation was pitted against nation in a very serious kind of war. Another kind of whist drive was the partner drive. Two people played as a team throughout the evening and in this case one had to be very careful about the choice of one's partner. One had to select someone with whom one had a strong rapport and someone strong enough not to become antagonistic if your abysmal playing helped to lose the game.

With close partners, there was always a temptation to cheat but the MC was always alert for this. He'd keep his sharp eyes open for the man who'd wink the left eye if he had the ace of shinners or the right if he hadn't a shinner in his hand. But a genuinely good whist partner had no need to cheat; a good partner was akin to a companion who was so close that the couple could almost thought-read. By the way one partner played his cards, the other could calculate which cards were held by the friend and which were held by the opposition. In this way, a tremendous amount of skill entered the game, and consequently whist, like many card games, was not classified as a lottery. It is a game of skill and chance combined, the chance being the hand of cards one is dealt, and the skill being the way in which the hand is played. The same applies to dominoes and cribbage, two very popular games, especially in pubs.

The villages around Aidensfield, therefore, were rich in highly skilled whist players. These moorfolk, men and women alike, had played whist since childhood and knew each other's game as if it was printing in large letters on their foreheads. So skilled were they, that they knew which cards the other would play in any given circumstance; they knew how to read the facial features, hand gestures, signs of worry like foot-tapping or nail-biting. And by memorizing the cards which had been played and the sequence in which they had fallen, they knew which cards remained to be played in any of the hands of the others at the table.

Players of this calibre, therefore, were steeped in the game and they could not tolerate unseasoned players joining 'their' whist drives. This was because those unseasoned players had not competed locally over an extended period, and so the established player did not know how to 'read' their game.

The result was that the strangers often won, simply because their unorthodox or amateurish style of card play completely perplexed and disorientated their more studious opponents. Many an old player has regaled a newcomer because of an awkward style of play, and so many new players refused to attend local whist drives. The aggravation, with its open criticism and rude comments, was just not worth it.

The result was, of course, that whist drives of that kind gradually ceased to exist; as those old players went off to that ever-winning whist drive in the sky, no young people took their places.

But schoolchildren are impervious to the niceties of adult behaviour or culture and, quite often, brash youngsters would attend these drives just for the sheer fun of annoying the hardened adult players. A rampant schoolboy with a hand full of shinners was indeed a menace, as was the quiet kid who knew how to read the game and confound his seniors by playing contrary to their own system.

It was memories of this kind that flooded back to me when I was visited by an old school friend called Dave. He had been working as an accountant for a British company in Africa for a few years and had returned to England for a three-month break, staying with his parents. We invited him to visit us for a few days. On the second day of his visit, I walked him through Aidensfield, showing him the historic church and other interesting parts.

We met some of the local people too, and had a lunch-time drink in the Brewers' Arms. It was there, on the pub notice board, that he spotted the poster which announced that a partner whist drive was to be held that evening in Aidensfield village hall.

'I think we ought to go.' His eyes twinkled as he read the details. 'Remember when we were kids, going to those partner drives and winning everything!'

It all came back to me. Dave and I would be about fourteen at the time, both living in a tiny moorland village where the only entertainment was the snooker table and the weekly whist drive. One night, we ventured into the hall as a whist drive was about to start and there happened to be two seats vacant at one of the tables. The MC spotted us and invited us to join the drive. It was a partner drive, he warned us, so we would have to play together as a team throughout the evening, but at least we did make up a full table. Thus we were regarded as useful.

Ever ready for a bit of juvenile excitement, we joined in and we actually enjoyed it. We could play whist – we played every day on the half-hour train journey to school and so this more formal approach held no fears for us. We did not, of course, bargain for the extremely serious approach which was adopted by these regular attenders; whereas our schoolboy game was a bit of fun, this was a very solemn affair.

But on that first occasion, we did our best; we didn't win anything, but we were invited back if and when there was a couple of spare seats. As it happened, there was often a couple of vacant seats and so Dave and I became regular players. And we began to win. We knew each other's play; very quickly, we learned to 'read' the method of play of the others and were soon attaining high scores, winning regularly and moving from table to table to tackle fresh opponents. We did not win at every drive, but we did do extremely well. We were good whist partners.

And so, all those years later when Dave visited me at Aidensfield on the very night of a partner drive, it seemed that this was an omen. We would attend for old time's sake, just for a bit of fun as we had done all those years ago. To be sure we wouldn't make complete fools of ourselves, we had some practice games at home with Mary and a dummy hand, and it was surprising how, after a dozen or so rounds, we regained most of our old skills. I found myself knowing how Dave would play.... I grew quite excited about tonight's game.

As we left the house that night, Mary warned me not to show off, for one of my long-time interests has been card manipulation and sleight-of-hand. I knew a lot of false deals, card-sharping and vanishing tricks but had no intention of using that knowledge or my conjuring skills at the village whist drive. But I did know enough about card-sharping never to play cards for money with total strangers.

At the door, Randolph Burley, the local auctioneer, hailed me and took our money.

'I didn't know you were a whist man, Mr Rhea,' he said.

'I'm not.' I decided to play down my past experience. 'But this is Dave, an old school friend. We used to play a bit on the train, on our way to school, so we thought we'd revive a few memories tonight.'

'It's a big night,' he said solemnly. 'There's a lot at stake – it's Steel Cup night.'

Joe Steel was the village shopkeeper and had donated the Steel Cup; it was to be won by the most successful partnership over the past year, and tonight two teams were competing for it. Each team had won on five occasions over the year; in twelve partnership drives, each had won five times. There'd been a stray winning team last November, thus ensuring a cliff-hanging finale. Tonight, the twelfth and last drive in the series, was the deciding match. Now two teams were drawing, but if neither of them won tonight the cup would be held over and they'd all have to start again next year. But some felt there would be a clear winner.

'It'll be Mr and Mrs Dunstone,' said Randolph. 'I reckon they've the edge on John and Mary Potter. It's a full house. Folks have come from far enough, so we've put out extra tables.'

And so we paid our entrance fees, obtained our score cards and entered the throng.

The gleaming silver Steel Cup stood on a table on the stage, and there was an array of other lesser prizes for tonight's game. A lot of the players raised their eyebrows at the sight of me among the tables and I'm sure they wondered what on earth I and the unknown man were doing there. In fact, Dave did look rather like a policeman and I'm sure they thought we were undercover constables on the look-out for cheats, this being such an auspicious occasion.

Dave and I did lose a few hands, but it was astonishing how the cards fell; we got some very good hands and we found that our past skills had not deserted us. If we weren't careful, this might be an embarrassingly successful evening.

It was.

We won.

In fact, we won handsomely, with me coming away with a bottle of malt whisky and Dave winning a box of groceries. But we had scuppered the Steel Cup. For the Dunstones and the Potters, the outcome remained a draw and they would have to start all over again next year.

In the days that followed, I found that I received a very cool reception from certain villagers; the warmth I'd experienced in the past had quickly evaporated and I wondered what I had done wrong. I hadn't arrested anyone for a trivial matter, I hadn't upset anyone that I could recall and neither had Mary.... I puzzled over this for a day or two and mentioned it to Mary.

She said I was imagining things, but I knew I was not; the current state of chilliness was real enough. There was definitely a new air of disdain towards the village constable in Aidensfield and district.

It was Randolph who enlightened me.

'They weren't at all happy about you and your pal winning that night,' he said. 'That's upset the regulars, Mr Rhea. No stranger ever comes in and wins like that, not even in a partner drive. And you're a stranger at whist-drives, not being a regular attender. You weren't supposed to win, Mr Rhea, with all due respect. Worse still, you and your pal stopped the Dunstones or mebbe the Potters winning that cup.... They said Mrs Dunstone was in tears afterwards – it would have been the culmination of a year's work for her and Alfred.'

I didn't know how to react or what to say. We'd played fairly and won fairly.

'We just went for a bit of fun, Randolph,' I told him. 'We didn't go to win or to deny anyone a cup or anything. We didn't even know about the contest till we got there.'

'Those players didn't see it like that,' he spoke solemnly. 'They reckoned you'd come in deliberately. Some said you were skilled whist men, you and that other chap, the way you played. They reckoned you were not beginners ... '

'We played as school kids,' I told him, and explained why we had decided to attend. Then I asked, 'So, how can I make amends?'

'There's no need,' he said. 'Forget it, they'll get over it. They start again next month, another year of couples aiming for the Steel Cup. It has to be won outright, you see. It's not given for draws.'

I went home and told Mary, but she said it was all my fault

for inviting Dave. 'You might have known you and he would cause trouble. Think of all those folks you beat as kids.... '

I thought about it and when I saw the following month's posters advertising the next partner drive, I called Dave. He was still staying with his parents in England and when I invited him over to Aidensfield to take part in another partner drive, he was delighted.

'My mother was pleased with those groceries,' he said.

'This time, it's not to win,' I cautioned him. 'I must let them beat me, they're not talking to me.... ' And I told the sorry tale.

'You're joking?'

'I'm not – just you come and see the reception we get if we go into the Steel Cup this time.... '

He came, as I knew he would. A frosty reception greeted us, but when we played hopelessly and lost game after game, the frostiness began to evaporate and the players, especially the Dunstones and Potters, began to smile. They nodded to one another with knowing grins ... these two men were not real players ... last time, it had just been luck ...

I could almost read their minds. I must say that Dave and I played magnificently. It was probably the finest partnership whist that we'd ever played, for we lost game after game most handsomely. We believed we'd played with extraordinary skill – I know the others thought we played like idiots and that our earlier win had been nothing more than a flash-in-the-pan. When I went to collect the wooden spoon on behalf of Dave and I, for achieving the lowest score of the night, I heard an old-stager say in a loud whisper.

'That'll teach 'em not to play whist against them who can play proper, them what really knows their cards!'

I smiled but decided I wouldn't show him my bottom deal or my range of false shuffles. Next day, the warmth had returned.

Indeed, a few whist fanatics invited me along to future drives, saying they'd teach me how to play properly if I was really interested, but I declined. 'It's far too complicated for me,' I said.

The wooden spoon was a most useful asset in our kitchen.

I'm sure one of our poets has said that love is a form of lottery, and when one learns how couples meet it seems it can be argued either that their meeting comes about through sheer lot or chance or that there is some other unknown power which brings them together. When I was a lad deep in the North York Moors, a high percentage of romances began through chance meetings at village dances which were always held in draughty halls.

The girls, like the wallflowers that many became, sat along one side of the hall while the youths stood at the other side, no shy youth daring to walk across that expanse of deserted floor to select a dancing companion. As the band, sometimes comprising only a fiddle and a piano, played waltzes, foxtrots, military two-steps and dashing white sergeants, so the lads tried to pluck up the necessary courage to ask a girl to dance. To do so meant a lonely walk across no man's land before the assembled audience, and that walk demanded courage of a very high order, especially if there was a likelihood that the girl would refuse the honour of dancing with such a noble fellow.

As a consequence, there were many occasions when the band played their entire repertoire for a particular dance and no one actually took to the floor. But the proverbial ice was usually broken when some youths, having obtained artificial courage at the pub, arrived to whirl the girls around to screams of delight. At this, the shy lads would respond and rush to the rescue of maidens whom they believed to be in distress.

One youth who was more shy than most was Geoffrey Stafford with whom I went to school. We were friends, but not close friends; perhaps a better word would be acquaintances for we never went around together as pals. But, like me, Geoffrey joined the police service and so, from time to time, I would come across him during my duties.

Geoff was memorable for several reasons. The first was his

inordinate shyness with girls, a second was his height for he was six feet seven inches tall, and a third was the size of his hands and feet. Quite literally, his hands were like shovels protruding from the sleeves of his clothing, sleeves which always seemed too short. At school, his jackets were always too short, with an enormous length of bare arm filling the space between the end of his sleeve and his wrist. Things hadn't changed as an adult – his police uniform sleeves were always too short, and when he stood to attention, it seemed as if his hands were so heavy that they were stretching his arms and drawing them out of their sleeves.

There were times when I wondered if the weight of his hands would drag his arms from their sockets.

But if his hands were huge, then so were his feet. To say they were colossal is an understatement. They were gigantic and fulfilled all those hoary old jokes about policemen having big feet. He took size fourteen in shoes, for example, and when his specially made uniform boots stood beside those of his colleagues, they looked like a pair of dug-out canoes each with a submarine conning tower at one end; they were large enough to have inspired the nursery rhyme about the old lady who lived in a shoe.

To witness Geoff patrolling down the street was indeed a sight to be treasured as those massive hands and feet worked in unison to propel his tall figure through the crowds.

To see him standing in the middle of the road directing traffic was equally memorable, for his huge mobile hands were like mechanical carpet-beaters, while his splendid feet anchored him safely when it was windy.

But for all his massive appendages, he was a charming fellow. He really did try to please people, and those who knew him did like and respect him, but his painful shyness with girls always militated against a successful romance. In an otherwise very happy life, that was the missing element, and he remained a reluctant bachelor. After all, for a neat-footed girl to do a quickstep with Geoff must have been like grains of corn trying to avoid being battered by flails.

I think it was his lack of success with girls and painful shyness that prompted him to join the Salvation Army. That uniform was just as ill-fitting as his police outfit, but I understand he was pretty effective with a pair of cymbals. His new-found faith, however, tended to restrict him even further in his search for romance because he ceased to join his colleagues in their pubs and clubs and stopped drinking alcohol.

It was one November when I met him during my duties. He had been seconded to the Crime Prevention Department and was going around shops and business premises advising them on internal security when he chanced to pass through Aidensfield. I was walking down the street in uniform and he hailed me. He, on the other hand, now wore civilian clothes, but they were as ill-fitting as his uniforms.

As he clambered out of his car, I was aware of that continuing gap which exposed a chunk of bare arm between his hands and his sleeves. He never did seem able to obtain jackets with sleeves long enough to cope with his endless arms.

We reminisced, as one always does on such occasions, and I reminded him of those village dances. He said he'd always enjoyed them, whereupon I said that Mary and I were going to the hunt ball next week: it was to be held in Aidensfield Village Hall and I was off duty that night. Several of us were forming a party – and I heard myself asking Geoff if he'd like to join us. Much to my surprise, he said he would. He did remind me that he was a teetotaller now, but I said it was nothing to apologise for; besides, the bar would offer soft drinks.

I said we'd meet him inside the hall at 9 p.m. that Friday night, then I went home to tell Mary the glad tidings. Her only comment was that she hoped he didn't ask her for a dance – she had memories of his efforts as a young man, for he'd ruined more than one girl's shoes by trampling all over them in his gallant attempts to musically co-ordinate the movements of his colossal feet.

Later, while reflecting upon that particular hunt ball, it was

Geoff's presence that caused me to ponder upon the lottery of life. Also attending the ball was Catherine Schofield, the daughter of Sir James and Lady Schofield of Briggsby Manor. She was up from London where she worked in an art gallery and had decided to accompany her parents. They were keen supporters of the hunt, but for Catherine it was a brave decision because she was not really known as a local girl – she'd been away at school and had also worked away, in addition to which her upper class lifestyle had segregated her from the attention of village Romeos. It was not surprising, therefore, that she was still single at the age of twenty-nine.

If one asks why she had not found a husband in London or among her own class, then it might have been owing to her appearance. Although her father was tiny, Catherine was well over six feet in height, and she was far from pretty. As featureless as a flagpole and just about as thin, she had no discernible breasts or hips and wore peculiar spectacles and a hairstyle that made her look twenty years older than she really was.

Her light brown hair was worn in a tight bun and she had a penchant for sensible shoes and all-embracing shapeless dresses. The villagers called her Keyhole Kate after a character in the popular comics of the time. The poor girl did look like something from the past, but, like Geoff, she was charming and she was blessed with a delightful sense of humour.

On the night of the hunt ball she needed every ounce of that humour because I was suddenly aware of Geoff advancing towards her, arms and feet carving a wide swathe through the crowds.

To this day, I have no idea what caused him to pluck up the courage to make that move, but I was amazed to see him asking her to dance. It was an Eva three-step. To say they presented an astonishing sight is perhaps an understatement, but the truth is that the lofty couple did circumnavigate the dance floor head and shoulders above the rest of us, and Geoff did so without Catherine or anyone else tripping over his feet.

By some miracle, he kept them under control. And an even more astonishing miracle was that, at the end of it, Catherine was actually smiling with pleasure.

After another two dances with her, he brought her across to our group and introduced her. He bought her a drink and escorted her to supper. Mary and I were delighted....

And so a most unlikely romance was born. As I watched them that night, I did wonder whether this particular lottery did have some unknown force controlling it, or was it sheer chance that brought Geoff and Catherine together?

During the evening, I could see Geoff relaxing, I could see his shyness evaporating before our eyes and I could see the happiness in Catherine's eyes too. Here was a man, taller than she, who could make her laugh and be happy. If he stood on her toes, she laughed about it and he laughed about it too. Afterwards, we invited him back to our house for coffee before he drove home, but he declined, saying he had been asked to visit Briggsby Manor for a good-night drink. I wished him well.

'Will he be able to come to terms with Catherine's family?' Mary asked me as we drank our nightcaps.

'I don't see why not,' I responded. 'Class barriers aren't so restrictive these days. And he is an intelligent lad, you know.'

'I wasn't thinking so much of that,' she said. 'I meant his non-drinking stance. They own a brewery – I think Catherine's a big shareholder in it. Will he find himself facing a conflict of conscience?'

'True love will overcome that!' I laughed.

And so it did. Geoffrey left the police force to marry Catherine and he gave up being a teetotaller; he drank champagne at his reception and they went to live in London. He was found a position within the family brewery business and is now managing director. He is no longer a member of the Salvation Army and his suits are not only made to measure – they are actually made to fit him!

The last time I saw him, there was no long gap between his cuffs and those gigantic hands. In life's lottery, Geoffrey had drawn a winning ticket.

6   Every Dog Has His Day

Brothers and sisters, I bid you beware,
Of giving your heart to a dog to tear.
                    Rudyard Kipling (1865–1936)

Although the strong and friendly relationship between an Englishman and his dog is almost legendary, there are those who mistreat Man's Best Friend. Town and country police officers, the RSPCA, veterinary surgeons and many others can relate horror stories of our inhumane treatment, not only of dogs, but of cats, pets of all kinds, farm animals and even wild creatures. Even in these enlightened times, sadists go badger hunting and killing domestic cats for fun; they torment tiny creatures with whom they come into contact and tease the docile. Villains have been known to set fire to the manes of horses in fields, to poke out the eyes of trusting donkeys, inflate frogs with straws and shoot crossbow bolts into swimming swans and ducks. And there is worse.

But so far as dogs are concerned, the dogs' homes of this country are full of tragedies. Unwanted Christmas presents and birthday gifts are abandoned and left to die; dogs are left without food and water or denied veterinary treatment. Happily, many of them find their way into the caring hands of the RSPCA and other good homes, but some are not so fortunate.

The on-going catalogue of cruelty is far too extensive to include in a book of this type, but it is fair to add that police officers do care for the ill-treated animals they encounter. For example, constables on patrol frequently come across stray dogs, and they are obliged to care for them, if only temporarily, until they can be provided with a new home or humanely put to death. Country police officers in particular come across wandering dogs which have been thrown out of cars in remote places simply because their owners no longer want them. Why go to the trouble of driving into the countryside to abandon one's pet? Why not take it to a dogs' home or some other animal sanctuary? The sick logic behind such callousness is baffling.

After living in a domestic situation, the miserable, confused animals, some little more than pups, are unable to fend for themselves in the wild. Some are shot in the belief they are sheep worriers, but many simply starve to death or get killed in accidents. Some are trapped in snares set for rabbits; others die painfully through eating poisoned carrion. A few of these castaways are fortunate because they are found and cared for, either by country folk and farmers or by those who take them into formal care.

If a person genuinely cannot cope with a dog, then it is refreshing when they do make the effort to find it a good home, but it ought to be said that police stations are not repositories for unwanted dogs, nor indeed any kind of animal.

On a temporary basis, the staff of a police station will care for a lost or stray dog, but eventually the unwilling visitor will be removed to the nearest dogs' home or, failing that, destroyed. A police station, therefore, is not the place to which one takes an unwanted dog for convenience.

I was faced with such a problem while performing a series of half-day duties in Ashfordly. I was in the market town during the absence of one of the local constables, and at 9 a.m. one morning in early June was in the office typing a report about a traffic accident when the door opened and a scruffy child appeared at the counter. She was a girl of about ten with beautiful dark brown eyes and lank, unwashed hair which might have been a stunning shade of auburn had it been clean and cared for. She wore a faded old dress with a floral pattern upon it and her thin legs and arms were bare. She had a pair of old sandals on her sockless feet and a silver-coloured bangle on her right wrist.

'Yes?' I peered over the counter at her.

'Oi've found this dog,' she said with more than a hint of an Irish accent. She was hauling on a length of rope at the end of which was a large and beautiful dog; it followed her into the office. I recognized the breed – it was a borzoi, otherwise known as a Russian wolfhound, and was something like a large, silky haired greyhound, standing almost three feet high.

The borzoi was once a favourite of the Russian royal family and was introduced to this country just over a hundred years ago when it became a fashionable dog to possess. Although it was bred in Russia specifically for wolf-hunting, it was welcomed in this country for its beautiful, elegant appearance. Ownership of a borzoi soon became a status symbol.

The dog's predominant colour is white, and the one standing before me had patchy fawn-coloured markings about its body. Its tail was silky and it had a long snout with the most gentle of eyes peering up at me. It looked nervous as it stood in the police station and was somewhat grubby in appearance. I reached over to pat it, but it shrank away from me. A sign of ill-treatment perhaps?

'Where did you find it?' I asked the child.

'On the road, near our camp.' She did not smile.

'Which camp's that?' I asked.

'Oi don't know what it's called,' she said.

'By camp do you mean those caravans just up the road from here?'

'Yes, we're travellers. Moi ma said Oi had to bring the dog in here.'

'Ah!' Now I remembered something. I recalled an entourage of filthy lorries, vans and caravans which had turned up one day about a fortnight ago. These were not true gipsies, but didicois, tinkers, scrap merchants, travellers or whatever. The council had been trying to move them on and we kept an eye on them because of their petty thieving and unsocial behaviour. Some of the smelly menfolk were prone to causing trouble in the pubs.

It was while I looked at that girl, that I realized I had seen the dog before. It was a striking animal, not one to be easily overlooked, and in my various patrols past that collection of awful vehicles, I had seen the dog tied to a tree. It had been there the whole time, for several days in fact, so this was no stray dog! This child was trying to get rid of it, I was sure!

I decided to put her to the test.

'What's his name?' I asked.

'Carl,' she said instinctively.

The dog did respond to the name, but not in the way that a loved dog would do: there was no wagging of its tail or signs of happiness, just a slight reaction, a twitching of its ears and a slight movement of its head.

'So your mum doesn't want Carl any more and told you to bring him here, eh?' I said.

'She said to say Oi'd found him … '

'Then I'm sorry, young lady, but we do not take dogs in just because people don't want them. You need the dogs' home. Now, what's your name?'

'Leela,' she said.

'Leela what?'

'Smith.' She had a captivating smile. It was amazing how many travellers were called Smith. Try serving a summons on one Jake Smith and dozens will step forward, smiling a challenge; they are impossibly cunning.

'OK, Leela, you take Carl back to your mother and say I would not take him. If she wants to part with him, she must take him to a dogs' home – tell her there's one in York. They'll look after him, we can't do that. Do you understand?'

'But mum said you look after lost dogs…. '

'We do. We look after lost dogs, Leela. Lost ones, not unwanted ones. So take him back to your mother, OK? He's a lovely dog, Leela. You can't want to give him away, surely?'

She shrugged her thin shoulders. 'He's all roight but he wants a lot of food and exercoise ... '

I did not ask how the family had obtained Carl, but I did persuade the child to leave the station and to take the lovely dog with her. I just hoped Carl would not be abandoned and that these travelling people would take him to a home where he would be cared for.

Two hours later, a squat, heavily built and very untidy woman stomped into the police station, and I saw that she was towing Carl behind her. She had the striking black eyebrows and hair of the Irish and dark brown eyes; once she would have been pretty. Now she was gross, unwashed and perspiring.

'Oi want yous to take this animal.' She plonked her end of the rope on the counter. 'It's a stray dog, mister. It's been following us for days.'

'It's not a stray, Mrs Smith,' I used what I guessed was her name. 'It's your dog and we are not a dogs' home. You'll have to take it to York or give it to a good home. We take in strays, he's not a stray.'

'He would be if Oi bloody well turned him loose ... '

'I think you care too much for him to do that,' I suggested. 'At least you tried bringing him here instead of just abandoning him. It shows you feel for him.'

'Look, constable, he needs a good home, a better home than we can give him ... '

'Where did you get him?' I asked.

'Oi told you, he's a stray, he just turned up,' and she waved her hands in an expression of helplessness. 'Oi don't know where he come from but we can't keep him. We're travelling all the time and there's nowhere for him.... '

I must admit I had mixed feelings about this. I would have liked to have taken the dog off her hands because her motive was sound. I was sure we could publicize Carl's plight so that someone would come forward to offer him a home. But I also knew that Sergeant Blaketon and the others had been keeping an eye on those grotty vehicles and had seen the dog. They would know he was not a stray and I would get myself into trouble if I accepted him. Besides, police stations were never intended to be alternative dogs' homes. I had to be firm; to accept him might start an avalanche of unwanted dogs. These travellers might want to dispose of other animals!

'I'm sorry, Mrs Smith,' I said. 'But I just cannot accept him, it's not allowed. If you take him to the RSPCA or some other sanctuary, I know they'll be delighted to receive him, he's such a lovely animal.... '

She glared at me for a long time, her subdued fury being contained in that massive body, and I expected a torrent of powerful Irish oaths to flow, but they did not.

'You'll be sorry for this!' and she snatched the rope and stalked out of the building and past the railings with the magnificent dog trotting at her heels. I watched her go along the street with just a feeling of regret. If I'd wanted a dog of my own, I wouldn't have refused that one ... he was a real beauty and he looked so docile, albeit in need of a good home.

When she'd gone, I locked up the office to undertake a foot patrol around the town before knocking off at 1 p.m. It was now approaching 11.45 and I had a few calls to make; there would be no problem filling that hour or so.

But when I returned to the station just before one o'clock I saw Carl sitting on the footpath. One end of his rope was tied to the police station railings. He looked at me as I approached and I detected just a flicker of a wag from his tail. I stopped at his side and patted his silky head.

'So who brought you this time, Carl?' I asked, looking up and down the street. There was no sign of the Irish woman or any other travellers, so I loosened his rope and led him into the police office.

We kept some tins of dog food and biscuits to feed our canine guests and I gave him something to eat while I completed my written work. He ate with some sophistication, not wolfing down the food as I might have expected, and wagged his tail when I offered him a bowl of water.

Before I left the office, I placed him in the kennel behind

the building and left a note to inform the incoming constable that we had a guest. I put an entry in the Stray Dog Register, saying the dog had been left tied to the police station railings and that I was trying to locate the owner.

On my way home for lunch, I drove past the site of the travellers' camp, but they had gone. All that was left was a pile of ghastly rubbish and some scorched earth where they had lit their fires. It was no good chasing them for I had no idea of the direction they'd taken and they probably had a long start anyway.

From home, I rang Ashfordly Police Station to tell PC Alwyn Foxton that I'd looked for the dog's owners without success.

'What a gorgeous dog!' he enthused over the telephone. 'Isn't he a gem?'

'He is,' I said. 'But what can we do with him, Alwyn? I'd hate to have him put down … '

'Leave it to me,' he said. 'I think I know someone who'll give him a good home. Remember that chap last week, the one whose Afghan hound was killed by that bus? He said he'd never find a dog as good as the one he'd lost, and he couldn't afford to go out and buy one. Well, I might persuade him to have a look at this one.'

'Carl's his name,' I said.

'No, it was something like Newport … '

'The dog I mean!' I laughed.

'How do you know that if it's a stray?' he asked pointedly.

So I told him the detailed story and he praised the travelling woman for her efforts to secure a place for Carl, but said he'd treat the dog as a stray. If Newport did not want Carl, then we'd make a fuss about him in the local papers. That would surely produce someone who'd love and cherish him.

That evening, Alwyn rang me.

'Carl's gone to a good home,' he said. 'Mr Newport said he looks like a pedigree animal … he's delighted.'

And so the story did have a happy ending. Some two weeks later, I saw Mr Newport walking Carl beside a local stream.

The dog's lovely silky coat had been beautifully groomed and Carl appeared to be in superb condition; dog and master looked the picture of happiness and contentment.

And when I said, 'Hello, Carl,' the dog wagged his tail.

*   *   *

Ownership of a large dog is one way of ensuring a moderate level of physical fitness.

Because large dogs must have regular exercise and lots of activity, then their owners can also benefit; they receive beneficial exercise and activity. It was this simple logic that came to mind one evening when I found myself off duty and having a drink with Chris Ellis.

Until that time, I knew him chiefly by sight. In his early thirties, he was a quiet, well-dressed man who worked for a local department store. He lived in Aidensfield and drove his second-hand mini into Ashfordly every day to work. His home was a tiny stone cottage tucked under the lee of the hill, where he had two small children and a charming, but mousey wife. She rarely mixed with the other young women but did send her two children, a boy aged three and a girl four and a half, to playgroup. As some of my children also attended the same group, I was acquainted with the family.

I liked Chris. He was a pleasant-mannered man who took life seriously, perhaps a little too seriously, but he did his best for his family. Although his wage was low, he kept a clean, tidy home and ensured that his family were well fed and content. And I knew his wife had a part-time job which helped to clothe the family.

On the evening in question, he and I were among half a dozen men who had volunteered to do a little maintenance to the Catholic church we all attended: the roof gutters needed cleaning, the path needed weeding, some woodwork needed a coat of paint and several other jobs demanded attention.

Father Luke had recruited a band of volunteers, and as we worked, I found myself alongside Chris Ellis. Afterwards, we all adjourned to the Brewers' Arms for a pint or two. I found myself telling Chris about my love of the North York Moors and highlighting some of the sights and scenes to be explored. He surprised me by saying he had never ventured onto the moors – I told him there were isolated streams where the children would love to play, castles and old abbeys to visit, some picturesque walks to undertake, beauty spots to admire, villages to potter around and craftsmen's premises to examine. I told him about some particular places where we took our children – places where they could roam without hindrance and paddle in the cool waters of crystal clear moorland streams. There were wild bilberries and brambles to pick in the autumn and basking adders to observe in the summer....

But although Chris had lived all his life on the southern edge of those moors, he had never ventured into their depths.

'I'd love to go, Nick,' he confessed to me over our drinks, 'but I haven't the time now. As a kid, we never had a car so Dad couldn't take us, but now that I manage to run an old car, I never have time to take a ride out there ... '

'But you must have!' I cried. 'What about weekends?'

'I work Saturdays,' he said. 'All day, in the shop. Wednesday is my half day, but Marie goes out on Wednesday afternoons to her little job while I look after the children. She takes the car, you see. She works for a plumber, does his book-keeping. It's not much, four hours a week, but it helps with clothes for the kids.'

'And Sundays?' I persisted.

'We go to my mother-in-law's for lunch and stay the afternoon.'

'Every Sunday?' I asked.

'Yes,' he said quietly. 'Every Sunday after Mass.'

My heart felt for him. 'You mean she asks you ... '

'Yes,' he nodded, sipping at his pint. 'We can't get out of it. She gets upset if we suggest not going. She can't see why we don't want to go ... to be honest, I'm pretty fed up. I mean, once every fortnight wouldn't be too bad, but every week ... ' and he shook his head almost in despair.

'You've tried to break the routine?' I asked.

'You bet I have. I have no parents now, so I can't use them as my excuse. But she's a widow, Marie's her only child and she insists on doing Sunday lunch for us all – she loves seeing the bairns. Sometimes, I think we're doing a Christian duty towards her, and sometimes I think it's a real pain … '

'She sounds very selfish to me,' I muttered. I could appreciate the woman's loneliness, but she ought to have some respect for her daughter's own needs and recreation. Marie's mother was rapidly making herself into a burden.

'I mean,' Chris went on. 'It's not as if she hasn't friends, she has lots. She goes to the WI, she's busy with flowers for the church and that sort of thing, so she's not totally alone like some old folks. She could invite some of her friends in – some other lonely person would love the chance for company at lunch.'

I commiserated with him and we bought more drinks. He poured out his agony to me and I felt it was probably the first time he had been able to do this: his wife would be biased towards her mother. As we grumbled into our pint pots, I heard myself saying,

'What you need, Chris, is a dog.'

'A dog?' he was puzzled.

'Yes, a big dog. One that needs lots of exercise. One that would benefit from long walks on the moors. One you could train to your own standards, or even show in local dog shows.… '

'Why would I want a dog like that?' he puzzled.

'To get you out of your mother-in-law's house on a Sunday,' I smiled. 'You'd need to train it, exercise it … '

'I can't afford to buy a dog like that,' he sighed.

'You'd get a good one from the dogs' home in York,' I told him.

And so he did. That February, he turned up with a beautiful golden retriever called Cassius and promptly set about training him and exercising him.

Very soon, Chris and Cassius were familiar figures about the village and along the neighbouring footpaths, often strolling beside the village stream or through the fields. One day, I asked how his new mother-in-law avoidance scheme was working.

'So far so good,' he beamed. 'I'm taking things slowly. I've not put it to the test yet, but I've told mother-in-law that big dogs need exercise and training. I said there are dog training classes at weekends and that I might have to miss lunch one of these Sundays.'

'And?'

'Well, she agreed, funnily enough. It seems her husband kept labradors and had to exercise them, so she knows about dogs ... '

In the weeks that followed, I kept in touch with Chris and his plot. Then, one Sunday, he'd told his mother-in-law that he could not come to lunch. Marie and the children would come as usual, but he had to attend a one-day dog-training course with Cassius. It was to be held in Malton.

Having been primed to that notion, mother-in-law accepted his story without question. It was the break he needed. Within a month, Chris was saying that Marie was needed at some of the classes. The instructor suggested she attend to familiarize Cassius with any regular commands she might have to make – the dog needed to know all his human companions for it must not become a one-person dog.

And so mother-in-law found herself looking after the children while Chris and Marie took Cassius to his classes. Then, quite deliberately, they omitted to tell her that there was no class on one Sunday. They let her believe there was. And so Chris and Marie went off for the day, alone.

That single outing, following the challenge of training Cassius at Malton, had finally persuaded Marie that they ought to have more time to themselves, more time away from her mother's constant and not-so-subtle demands.

With Cassius quoted as the reason for missing that Sunday lunch, it was Marie who suggested to Chris that they take the children out and show them the moors, to show them sights she had only just discovered. They could play with Cassius in the streams and among the heather, and with summer coming along there would surely be some wonderful outings....

Chris was delighted, especially as the idea had come from Marie, but it backfired. Marie's mother insisted on coming too. Once she heard that Chris, Marie and the children were going out for a picnic, she invited herself along. It was a crush in the car, with mother-in-law, two children and Cassius on the rear seat, but there was no option.

Thereafter, mother-in-law inflicted herself upon Chris and Marie – she even went to the dog-training classes when they resumed.

'At least we get out of doors,' Chris smiled ruefully one day when he told me all this. 'It's better than sitting indoors all day, and we do see something of the countryside. But she won't leave us alone ... not even for a day!'

'You'll have to take Cassius for very long walks, then,' I laughed.

And so he did.

He told mother-in-law that they were going for a twelve-mile hike across the moors with Cassius, and invited her to join them. She declined, saying there was no way she could cope with such a trek at her age, and offered to look after the children. And so off went Marie, Chris and Cassius once again, but it seems the children were not too happy about that arrangement. Having tasted a world beyond granny's front room, they made their noisy, argumentative presence felt until she did not enjoy them at all. They wanted to be with their mum, dad and Cassius and they let their grandma know in no uncertain way – the good children of those earlier days had changed into noisy, demanding kids.

Then, one week, mother-in-law suggested that Chris and Marie take the children out with them; she'd stay at home, by herself, alone, with nothing to do and no one to see. If nobody wanted her, she would cook lunch for herself. She'd sit and watch television, all by herself. She'd do some knitting. She might do the washing, seeing she was alone....

'I know she's piling on the agony, but we've got to make the break,' Chris had told Marie yet again. And so they did. Marie now appreciated that they must not allow her mother to dominate their lives, and so they left her alone that Sunday while they took the children and Cassius onto the moors.

The last time I saw Chris, his weekends had fallen into a new pattern – he had given up dog-training classes, but he and his family did avoid the trap of being committed for lunch every Sunday with mother-in-law. It was not easy – they had to be alert to all her ploys – but they did visit her, they did take lunch with her once a month or so, and they did have picnics with her and the children. But all were enjoyable occasions, not imposed upon them by Royal Command.

'It's all thanks to Cassius,' he smiled one day.

But I did wonder what would happen when Cassius was too old to go for long walks. Would mother-in-law look after him while the others went out?

No one knew, but I was pleased to see that this young couple had learned to be as cunning as mother-in-law.

* * *

Britain is rich in stories of dogs whose faithfulness to their master or mistress has become part of our folklore. One of the best known is surely Greyfriars Bobby, a terrier owned by a Borders shepherd called Jock Gray. When Mr Gray died in 1858, Bobby went to his grave in Greyfriar's churchyard in Edinburgh and watched over it.

He remained at that graveside until he died in 1872, an astonishing period of fourteen years. He was fed by the local people and adopted by the city as a mascot. Upon his death, he was buried beside his master. A fountain near the church bears a statue of Greyfriars Bobby and that tiny dog's unfailing loyalty to his master has been a talking point ever since; his statue is now one of the tourist attractions of Scotland's capital city.

But many villages and towns offer similar stories of dogs,

albeit lacking the sheer endurance of Bobby. One such dog was a Border collie owned by a retired Aidensfield farm worker. The dog was a black and white sheepdog, locally known as a cur. These dogs are very popular with the sheep farmers of the Yorkshire dales and moors for they are hard working, very devoted and highly intelligent. The dog's name was Roy. His master was called Douglas Grisedale. Doug had laboured on local farms all his life and had retired, with his wife, to an old folks' bungalow in Aidensfield. He was a frail-looking man, hardly the robust character one tends to associate with heavy farm work. Very slender, with gaunt cheeks and dark eyes, he had retained his black hair even though he was going on for seventy. Doris, his wife, was a round and cheerful lady with pink cheeks and plump legs; she liked being busy and involved herself with all manner of organizations. She helped to run the village hall, she cleaned the church, joined the WI, became a parish councillor and so on.

Doug, on the other hand, was a quiet man who preferred to be alone, a legacy of his years of solitary work in the fields. He occupied his time with his bees and his garden and seemed quite content with his very peaceful retirement.

His constant companion was his dog, Roy. Although Roy was a sheepdog, he had never been used for shepherding, although from time to time he did reveal his natural instinct by rounding up hens and ducks in the village, then lying to watch over them as he contained them in the corner of a paddock. Doug would call him away and the dog would release his captives.

Man and dog went everywhere together. If Doug walked down to the post office for his pension or across to the pub for a pint and some tobacco, then Roy would accompany him. Doug seldom spoke to Roy, although he would sometimes say 'sit' or 'stay' and the dog would obey without hesitation. At other times, we would hear Doug say, 'Come on, awd lad', or 'Shift thysen, awd lad'. Awd lad was a term of endearment, meaning 'old boy'.

Roy was not a young dog; he had accompanied Doug during the latter years of his work on the farm and I guessed he would be around nine or ten years old when I first encountered him and his master. In observing them, it seemed as if there was some mental telepathy between the two because if Doug turned left or right, the dog did likewise at exactly the same time. Sometimes, it was uncanny to watch them.

On one occasion I saw them walking towards the post office when the dog suddenly stopped outside a cottage and sat down on the footpath. There had been no command from Doug; indeed, he continued along his way to leave Roy sitting alone. Then I saw a lady calling from the upstairs window of that cottage. She was trying to catch Doug's attention. Within seconds, her loud voice had halted him, but Roy was already waiting ...

The lady, a friend of Doug and Doris Grisedale, had seen him passing and wanted him to bring her some stamps. Had she called to Doug from inside the house so that, at first, he had not heard her voice? Could that call have been heard by the dog? Did the dog respond to a call of 'Doug' as it would have responded to its own name? Or maybe Doug had heard the call and was spending a few moments debating whether or not he should obey it? Had Roy made up his mind for him? We shall never know. It was a minor incident, but rich with interest; a curious example of the rapport between Doug and his dog.

In following his master everywhere, Roy's patience was endless. Whenever Doug went to the toilet, for example, Roy would lie outside the door and wait, even if it took Doug half an hour. I was to learn that the dog even slept outside Doug's bedroom door and that when he sat in at night to watch television, Roy would lie at his feet; but if Doug moved, Roy was on his feet in an instant, ready to follow wherever his master went.

Whenever Doug went to the post office or into Ashfordly for some garden seeds or equipment, Roy would go with him and wait outside the premises.

Their companionship spanned the years and then, one fateful morning, I spotted Roy lying outside the surgery. He was stretched out with his chin on the threshold of the door which stood open and I knew Doug must be inside. Indeed he was; it was a rare event for him even to speak to a doctor let alone visit one, and I wondered what was the problem. But I didn't ask. After all, in the twilight of their years, many men did have problems and ailments which could benefit from a doctor's wisdom.

But the next thing we knew was that Doug was being whisked off to a hospital in York for tests. It was decided to detain him there. No one spoke openly of their worries about Doug because one never likes to air one's hidden fears, but it was Doris who hailed me soon afterwards. She caught me as I was filling the tank of the police van at the garage.

'Mr Rhea,' she said, 'Roy's run away. I've tried to keep him in but he got out the day before yesterday. I've looked everywhere Doug used to sit or go, but I can't find him.'

'He'll be pining for Doug, is he?'

'Aye.' There were tears in her eyes. 'Aye, he is,' she said quietly. 'They're inseparable, those two.'

'I'll put a note in our books. We'll ask our lads to keep their eyes open,' I promised her. 'Has he got a collar on?'

'Aye, with our name and address on it,' she nodded. 'Doug said we'd better do that if Roy was coming to live in a village.'

'Good. It'll help if he has wandered off.'

It was next day when I got a call from York Police.

'PC Stevenson, York City,' said the voice. 'We've got a stray dog here, a sheepdog, with the name Grisedale, Aidensfield on the collar. They're not in the telephone directory so can you call and ask them to pick him up? He's a lovely dog, but a bit thin and dirty. We wouldn't want to see him stuck away in the dogs' home.'

'Where was he found?' I asked.

'Hanging about at the County Hospital. He's been trying to get inside. They found him in one of the corridors and brought him down to us.'

'His master's in there,' I said softly, with more than a hint of tears in my eyes. 'Keep him safe, will you? I think he's walked all the way to York to be with Doug ... '

'You're joking! It's all of twenty miles!'

'I'll be in touch,' I assured him after telling him about Roy's devotion.

Doris did not drive, and I could hardly justify use of the official van to drive into York to collect the dog, so when I went to inform Doris that Roy had been found, I said,

'Doris, you'll be wanting to visit Doug, won't you? So if I drive you in this evening when I'm off duty, I can leave you at the hospital while I pop down to Clifford Street to collect Roy. Then I can fetch you both back home.'

'That would be nice, Mr Rhea,' she smiled. 'I get the bus in as a rule.'

While I was with her, I remembered to pick up a lead for Roy.

Our local bus went to York on Tuesday, Thursday and Saturday mornings and returned in the afternoons, so poor Doris would not see much of Doug, although I knew that several of the villagers would take turns to drive her in. My offer was therefore accepted with pleasure. It was during that drive into York that I learned the truth about Doug's condition – he had cancer of his intestine. It had only just been discovered but it was so far advanced that he would not survive. It must have been eating away at his innards for months, perhaps years. But he had never complained. If only he'd gone to a doctor earlier ... he must have known things weren't right ... I learned he had only a short time to live, six months at the most. Doris was very brave about it.

I dropped her off at the hospital and went to the Clifford Street headquarters of York City Police to collect Roy. He recognized me, but he was thin and dirty, not the handsome dog I knew so well. But he jumped into my car without any trouble and sat on the front seat as I drove back to the hospital.

Even as I approached, his mood began to change; he

whimpered and wagged his tail, looking at me as if trying to ask me something, and I knew what he wanted. He wanted to visit Doug. That's why he had walked all the way to York, without food or shelter....

'I'll see what I can do, awd lad.' I used Doug's own phrase as I patted Roy on the head.

I went into the office on Ward 4 and was fortunate to find the duty doctor, Dr Holt. I explained about Roy's adventure and I could see the doctor was moved. He went so far as to say that the presence of the dog might cheer up Doug who was miserable in his enforced inactivity. I did explain that Roy was, at this moment, somewhat dirty after his escapade, and did remind him that Roy had already been here of his own accord, hoping to visit Doug. Holt remembered the dog ...

'We had no idea.' He shook his head. 'We thought he was just another stray nicking scraps from our wastebins ... but even if we'd caught him and seen the name on the collar, I doubt if anyone would have linked the two.... '

I felt sure that Roy's visit would not be a surprise to Doug because Doris would have told him, but as I led him into the ward and released his lead he galloped directly to the room in which Doug lay. He knew exactly where to go. The emotion of their reunion was overwhelming, not only for Doris and me but for all the occupants of that small ward, men who had learned of Doug's attachment to his dog. They and their visitors wept as the crying Doug fondled his dog's ears and the happy Roy made a fuss of his master. The meeting had a powerful effect upon all of us. Then everyone cheered up. The other patients wanted to meet Roy, they wanted Doug to tell them about him; some were city people who knew nothing of the relationship between a farm worker and his dog. They wondered how on earth he could have found his way from Aidensfield to York – that was something no-one could determine. And as I watched, wiping my own eyes, I knew we could not separate the two, not now. Not after what Doris had told me. As the couple and their dog made friends with everyone, I slipped out to find Dr Holt.

'I saw what happened,' he said quietly. 'It's astonishing.'

'You know my next request?' I put to him.

He nodded. 'It's not been done before – hygiene, you understand. Dogs are not really allowed in the hospital, let alone in the wards, and he is more than a bit scruffy.'

'Doug would soon put that right,' I said. 'Roy is house trained and he would not come into the ward unless he was allowed. This really is an amazing relationship. Roy would lie outside all day, just waiting. He'd need the occasional walk, that's all, and some food ... Doug would see to that.'

'Doug's not fit to see to that, Mr Rhea,' said the doctor. 'He is a very sick man, more than his wife realizes, more than he realizes.'

'But not more than Roy realizes?' I said.

'Point taken. OK, the dog can stay,' Dr Holt said. 'I will clear it with the authorities ... '

'Doug will tell Roy what to do, how to behave and so on,' I assured him.

And so, contrary to hospital regulations, Roy was allowed to remain. The nurses fell in love with him and he had no shortage of walks. One of them bathed him to clean him up and they took turns to feed him. Another found some old discarded blankets and made him a bed outside the ward door. But Roy never ceased his observations of Doug. As predicted, he spent his time lying just outside the door of the ward, his nose to the floor as he watched the passing events inside.

At visiting time, he was allowed in – he went in whether or not anyone escorted him, following the other visitors even if Doris was not there. In those final days of Doug's life, man and dog were happy; there was no doubt that the dog's presence did help to ease that time for Doug. But after less than two weeks, the ailing Doug passed away in his sleep. Dr Holt knew because Roy began to whine and ask for admission to the ward, but there was nothing anyone could do.

At the funeral, Roy walked beneath the coffin as the bearers carried it towards the altar, and during the service the vicar allowed Roy to lie on the altar steps, his eyes always on the coffin. After the service, he again walked beneath the coffin on the way out to the churchyard, tail between his legs.

He whined miserably as the coffin was lowered into the dark earth and uttered a weird, heart-rending howl as the vicar threw a handful of loose earth onto the coffin. Then, like Greyfriars Bobby, Roy lay down beside the grave and refused to move. In spite of pleas from Doris and her friends, he would not go home to eat or drink nor would he touch any food brought to him. He simply faded away.

Roy died three weeks after Doug and the vicar allowed him to be buried in the same grave. Later, when the family erected Doug's tombstone, there was an addition to his epitaph.

Beneath the inscription to Doug's memory, there were the simple words: *'Roy, his friend – 1953–1966.'*

7   Men of Letters

Aidensfield and the villages which surround it are most fortunate with their postmen and postwomen. The service they provide has always been infinitely more than the mere delivery of letters and parcels, and this is because the postie, as he or she is affectionately known, visits every home in the area. The postie does not visit every home *every* day of course, but because of the nature of their job, these uniformed messengers are in a unique position to meet everyone and to become aware of any social problems that might arise. This is especially so among the lonely, the elderly and the infirm.

One of the finest ways for a lonely pensioner to gain the attention of the postman is to offer him a cup of tea or coffee during his rounds. Here in North Yorkshire, our mail comes early – mine arrives between 7.15 a.m. and 7.45 a.m. as a rule and we do receive it on time. Some Londoners think our papers arrive a day late and our letters spend a week in transit! This is not the case – in my morning mail, I receive lots of letters date-stamped the previous day in London and elsewhere, even those bearing second-class stamps. For us, the service is superb, especially as it is carried out on such a personal basis.

The postman knows us and we know him. I know that if we are away, he'll leave the mail next door or even keep it until we return; if we're still in bed when he arrives, he'll tuck it under

the front step or even call back if the morning weather is likely
to harm any mail he leaves for us. He will take the trouble to
decipher difficult handwriting or incorrect addresses, and he'll
share our joy when postcards arrive from friends in exotic
places, or commiserate with us when we get final reminders
from the income tax authorities or the electricity people. He'll
say 'I see your Aunt Agatha's leg is getting better' or 'What's
that lad of yours doing in Sri Lanka?' This kind of relationship
is not regarded as prying, for, in a village community,
knowledge of another's life-style and habits can sometimes be
a life-saver. Any good policeman knows that – as does the
nurse, the doctor, the vicar and, of course, the postman.

Even in the depths of winter when snow, ice or fog can
render other services impotent, the post manages to get
through and so it maintains the enviable reputation of the
Royal Mail. Few of us bother to say 'thanks' for this
remarkable achievement – but we do blame the postman if the
letters we are expecting bring bad news! This harks back to
primitive times when emperors executed messengers who
delivered bad news! We still blame the man who carries the
letter rather than the person or organization that wrote it.

Here in North Yorkshire, with vast uninhabited areas to
cover along with daily visits to isolated farms and cottages, our
postmen must begin their day very early. Some occasional
deliveries involve a trek of up to two miles through
countryside that is rough enough to make a fine training
ground for tanks, or remote enough to be utilized as a practice
range for firing cannons. Consequently the delivery of some
letters can be a tiring and long-drawn-out affair. By ten
o'clock in the morning, therefore, most rural postmen (and in
that term I include postwomen) are ready to sit down with a
cup of hot tea and a biscuit. And it is a wise person who offers
that kind of sustenance and sanctuary. The benefits can be
tremendous.

This is where the lonely or house-bound person can score
lots of Brownie points with the postman. A cup of tea or coffee
and a hot, buttered scone can be like a feast to a tired and

footsore postal delivery operative, especially on a wintry day. And, in return, the postman will offer to undertake small chores. I know one lady pensioner in a moorland village who feeds passing postmen with meals large enough to be described as banquets; in return they do her shopping and run her messages. As she cannot easily get to the shops or call on tradespeople, the postman of the day will take her order and obtain the necessaries, delivering them when next he calls for his coffee and buns. It is an admirable arrangement.

I know of postmen and postwomen who light fires for pensioners, who feed dogs and cats for people at work, who collect laundry, shopping, dry-cleaning and pensions, who change library books, collect eggs and deliver sacks of potatoes or turnips. One collects fish-and-chips on Fridays and another checks the snares laid by a farmer who is rather lame – that postie's reward is the occasional rabbit or hare. This is a most useful kind of barter system, and it helps to keep a community happy and in touch with one another. In these modern times, the postman can quite easily store a sack of potatoes or a case of wine in his van for delivery to a local house; in the good old days, it would not have been so easy, for there was a limit to what could be carried on a postman's bike or in the sack on his back.

But there was one postman who had another kind of regular commitment, one which I did not know about for some time. He was Postie Win. His name was Winston Charlesworth, a man whose unfortunate initials had earned him the childhood nickname of Closethead. Even at that time, the mid-1960s, not every village home had a water closet or WC as they were known; some continued to use the earth-closets, sometimes known as thunder-boxes, johns or necessaries, abbreviated to nessies.

Winston had the sense to make fun of his own name and initials, and this confounded those who tried to mock him. As he matured, he wooed and married a local girl, but for some reason they had never produced any children.

This was sad because Winston had come from a large and

caring family and loved children – he was Father Christmas at village parties and was a friendly character who bred rabbits and guinea pigs in his tiny back garden.

Winston earned his living as the postman for Elsinby, covering several tiny villages, including Waindale, Ploatby and Thackerston. He knew everyone and they knew him; he was the kind of good-hearted fellow who would undertake any of the chores I have already mentioned but who expected nothing in return. His tastes were simple and he was always whistling and singing as he went about his multifarious jobs. And to do his work, he rode a red post-office bicycle with a large front tray which sometimes seemed too full of parcels to be safe on the roads. Yet he coped, even if he did sometimes wobble.

Like all his rural colleagues, his round began very early each morning, about 6.30, and when I was undertaking any of my early patrols, we would often meet. We would stop for a chat and would swop yarns – we'd mention people we knew who might have developed the need for a quiet helping hand, or if there had been any crimes in the locality; I would ask if he'd seen any suspicious characters in the area. In his work, he saw far more than I, and so I could warn him of outbreaks of housebreaking, damage or vandalism, and he told the householders to beware of strangers and to lock up their goods. He kept a constant eye open for malefactors and we had a good mutual understanding.

I found it odd, therefore, one Friday morning, when I couldn't find him. There had been a hit-and-run accident near Elsinby; I knew he would be in the village, so where had he gone? I needed to find him urgently to ask him about the incident.

The reason for my anxiety began about 7.15 a.m. one late January morning. A 22-year-old girl called Jenny Green was riding her bicycle from Ploatby to Elsinby along the narrow lane which linked the two communities. It was a frosty morning and there were patches of ice on the roads; furthermore, it was dark, but Jenny knew the dangers and was

riding carefully. She was on her way to Elsinby to catch the
7.30 a.m. bus to York where she worked in a shop. It was a
trip she undertook every working day, even on Saturdays. She
returned early on Wednesdays, however, that being her
half-day. Each day, she left her bike in a shed behind the
Hopbind Inn and rode home after work, her return bus
arriving just after six o'clock. It was a long day, but she
claimed she enjoyed the work and the chance to be involved in
a city environment.

On that Friday morning, she had been riding along the
correct side of the road, with her bike properly illuminated,
when a car had approached her from behind. Jenny, upon
hearing the car and seeing the spread of its lights about her as
it came nearer, had eased to the left so that she was almost
riding on the verge. But the front wing or some other part of
the car had collided with her right handlebar; the impact had
unbalanced Jenny and thrown her off her bike and into the
hedge. The offending car had not stopped, but in her distress,
Jenny had not noticed any material details; she couldn't even
say whether it was a large or small, red or blue, Austin, Ford,
Vauxhall or Rolls-Royce, nor had she noticed its registration
number.

Fortunately, Jenny wasn't badly hurt although she did
suffer a few cuts and bruises and a lot of scratches from the
thorns of the hedge. Her clothes were also torn, she had
ripped her nice winter top coat, and the front wheel of her
bike was buckled. She was more angry than injured and
hurried to a nearby cottage for help. I was told about the
accident some twenty-five minutes after it had happened, long
enough for the offending car to reach York and get lost in the
traffic, but I hurried to Jenny's parents' home in Ploatby. I
found her battered bicycle outside with Jenny in the kitchen,
sipping a cup of hot sweet tea as her mother fussed like a
broody hen. I established that she did not need medical
attention; Mum would see to the scratches.

I tried to take firm details but Jenny could not provide me
with any hint as to the identity of the car; the only thing she

could say was that it had never passed her on any previous morning. Normally, no one passed her during that short ride. Only when she reached Elsinby did she see other people and cars.

That morning, of course, she hadn't got as far as Elsinby and so no one there could help.

She was adamant that the car's nearside mudguard or even its wing-mirror had touched her handlebar and unbalanced her, and from that I doubted whether the car would be damaged. Maybe the driver had no idea he'd touched her? That was possible – if his wing mirror had caused the problem, the smallest touch could have unbalanced Jenny. I finished up with no description of the offending car, other than it was well illuminated and it was not driving at excessive speed. That tended to rule out a stolen vehicle being used by a joy-rider.

Nonetheless, I rang our Sub-Divisional office to circulate the car as being involved in a hit-and-run accident, thinking that if the car was going about some illicit mission it might attract attention elsewhere. I realized that it must have driven through Elsinby moments after upskittling Jenny, so perhaps someone there had noticed it? Someone like Postie Win?

By the time I had taken Jenny's statement, measured the scene and circulated details, it was almost nine o'clock, and when I began inquiries in Elsinby, most of the people who'd been around at 7.30ish had gone to work. But Postie would be around.

I began to look for him, hoping to catch him emerging from a cottage, but I never saw him. Nor did I see his familiar red bike. I began to grow concerned – I hoped the offending car had not knocked him off his bike too!

Was he lying hurt in a ditch somewhere? Had he been knocked into the stream which ran through the village? Was he lying in a hedge, or unconscious in someone's back garden? I toured Elsinby in my van, looking for Postie and his bike, but failed to find him. I must admit I was growing worried, for he was *always* delivering in the village around this time. Just after 9.15, I decided to call at his home. Perhaps he was ill? I had to know.

Mrs Charlesworth answered my knock. 'Is your Win about?' I asked.

'He'll be at the school,' she smiled, checking her watch.

'Of course!' I had forgotten about the school. It lay half a mile out of Elsinby along a narrow lane, and because there were no cottages there, I'd forgotten he might call there with any letters and had omitted to search that area. I told Mrs Charlesworth the reason for my call and she said she'd ring the Greens to ask after Jenny; maybe she'd need some ointment picking up from the chemist's? Win would see to that if she asked him....

As I drove towards the school, I was relieved to see the familiar red bike leaning against the wall with its front tray full of parcels and letters. As I climbed from my van to walk towards the school I could hear the children singing their morning hymns: it was assembly time. And then, as I reached the gate, I could see Postie Win.

He was standing at the head of the class, conducting the children and singing louder than them, thoroughly enjoying a spirited rendering of 'Dear Lord and Father of Mankind'. And he had a superb voice. I wondered whether to go in … but he spotted me and beckoned me inside. I decided I could justify this intrusion because I could ask if any of the children had seen the car – it was hardly likely, but some youngsters did get up early to feed their ferrets or rabbits, walk their dogs and milk their goats.

The headmistress smiled a welcome.

'Hello, Mr Rhea. Come in. We're just finishing assembly.'

'I see you've got a good singer there!' I laughed.

'Winston always comes to sing with us,' she said. 'Every morning. He leads the children in their hymns.'

At this, Winston joined us. 'I love a good sing-song,' he said. 'Well, I must be off.'

I halted him and told the story of the hit-and-run, but he couldn't help – he hadn't seen the car. With the teacher's help,

I asked the children too, but they all shook their heads. I thanked them for helping me and the headmistress asked me to call back sometime, by prior arrangement, to tell them about my work. I said it would be a pleasure. I walked out with Winston and he said he'd keep his eyes and ears open for the car; maybe it was a newcomer to the area, maybe this was his first day at work and he was rushing ... it was all maybes.

'Thanks,' I said. 'And well done, singing like that with the children.'

'I love a good sing-song,' he laughed. 'Singing with those kids gives me a marvellous start to the day. I call in every morning. You can't beat a bit of hymn-singing with the bairns to remind you what life's all about. Well, I must be off.'

'Where to now?' I asked.

'Old Mr Coates,' he said. 'I light his fire for him every morning. Then it's Miss Bowes. Her washing machine's playing up – I think it needs a new belt so I said I'd fix it ... '

'It's a busy life, being a postman,' I laughed.

'Being a postman's the easy bit!' he chuckled as he rode off. And then he called, 'I'd better pop in to see if Jenny Green wants anything, eh? Maybe her bike needs fixing!'

I was to learn that he had straightened the buckled front wheel by the simple expedient of laying the wheel flat on the ground and jumping on its rim. It had sprung back into shape. Jenny took the following day, a Saturday, off work and resumed on the Monday, riding her bike as usual to catch the bus.

I had learned a little more about the philosophy and routine of a local postman, but we never did find that offending car.

* * *

Mortimer Micklethwaite was another rustic postman, but his achievements did not meet the high standards of those undertaken by Postie Win.

In fact, Mortimer's achievements were practically nil because he was no good at anything. Born to ageing parents, and having suffered the trauma of being born in an era when medical care was not of a high standard, poor Mortimer was one of life's losers. Some said that if he'd been a tup lamb or a bull calf, he'd have received better care from the vet than he did from the aged midwife who'd delivered him.

Some said his mother had been frightened by a mad donkey just before Mortimer's birth, some said she'd seen a ghost as Mortimer was entering the world, and others claimed she'd seen the devil himself, but whatever had gone wrong at birth had resulted in Mortimer being rather simple. His mental capacity was likened to that of a frog, so by no stretch of the imagination could Mortimer be described as a bright lad. Locally, it was said he was as fond as a scuttle, as empty as a blown egg, as daft as brush or as soft as putty. In Yorkshire, the word *fond*, in this instance, means stupid. Poor Mortimer was rarely flattered or praised.

He and his parents lived in Crampton where his father had a joiner's shop tucked away behind a huddle of red-roofed limestone cottages just off Dale Street. Arthur Micklethwaite was a craftsman, there is no doubt about that, and one of my joys was to visit his workshop, there to watch him at work amid the powerful scents of seasoned timber and wood shavings. His workshop was always warm, even in the depths of winter, and he never seemed to hurry yet always delivered commissions on time.

He did a lot of work for Crampton Estate and his immaculately finished products ranged from superb dining furniture to five-bar farmyard gates via coffins and church benches. He'd even made cart-wheels as a lad and was still a proficient wheelwright, sometimes creating them for people who wanted them to adorn their gardens and patios. A visit to Crampton today will reveal many of Arthur's cart-wheels still adorning village walls and gardens.

But when I first knew Arthur, he was well into his eighties, albeit still working, while Mortimer was getting on for forty. To Arthur's credit, he had tried to teach Mortimer his craft, but I knew from village gossip that Mortimer could not absorb

any of his father's tuition. He was just too thick, but he did
continue to help his father, often being allocated simple tasks
like sweeping the floor, chopping up end-bits for firewood or
even priming bare timber prior to being painted. But he could
never be trusted to make anything, not even something basic
like a toothbrush holder or bookends.

Within a couple of years of my arrival at Aidensfield, Arthur
had died, leaving his business to Mortimer. After all, he was
Arthur's only son, and with a bit of coaxing from his mother,
Annie, the lad might just be able to scrape a living. But Annie
was also in her eighties and a little frail and although she did
know a lot about the running of the business, she was unable
to provide Mortimer with the necessary full-time guidance.
But Mortimer did try.

One brave householder, a newcomer to the village,
commissioned Mortimer, now hailing himself as Crampton's
Cabinet Maker, Undertaker and Wheelwright, to replace
some rotten window frames. A local person would never have
taken that risk but Mr Slater, a retired businessman from
Liverpool, did not know of Mortimer's weaknesses and
believed in making use of rural craftsmen. The task was
simple – three cottage-style windows along the front of Mr
Slater's country home had rotten frames which must be
replaced. Mr Slater would be away for two weeks during
which time the work could be done. Mortimer, so proud at
being asked to do such an important job, said he'd fix them.

I was in the village when Mortimer's handiwork was being
fitted into the gaping hole from where he had removed the first
window. I halted out of curiosity, my interest being aroused
by the sight of the diminutive Mortimer actually doing some
work. One of his father's old friends was helping.

Mortimer, a mere five feet tall with a long face and thin,
sandy hair, was clad in his father's old apron with an array of
tools in the front pocket like a kangeroo's pouch. The two men
were attempting to fit the window frame into the gaping hole.
But from my vantage point at the other side of the road, it was
clearly impossible. Mortimer's newly made window, devoid of

glass, was far too small for the hole they had created by removing the existing one, and it was the wrong size for either of the remaining two window spaces.

'Thoo's got all t'measurements wrong!' grunted the helper.

'Turn it round sideways then,' said Mortimer.

'Thoo daft ha'porth, that's neea good! Tonning it sidewards only makes it worse! Onnyroad, some of these spaces thoo's made for t'glass is inside out! By, thoo's made a right pig's ear of this job, Mortimer!'

To cut a long story short, Mrs Micklethwaite hired another local carpenter to make and fit the new windows; she would pay him out of the fees to be paid by Mr Slater.

And so the job was done in time for Mr Slater's return.

When Slater saw the handiwork, he was delighted.

'You know,' he said in the pub later, 'it's nice to see the work of a genuine craftsman. You don't get such skills in Liverpool. So, I shall be asking Mr Micklethwaite to undertake more work for me.'

Everyone was so astonished that they said nothing. In fact, due to his mother's influence, Mortimer did just that. Every-time he was asked to do a carpenter's task, his mother commissioned a neighbouring craftsman, and so Mortimer became a middleman and, with his mother's help, did manage to earn a meagre living. In the meantime, while his 'workers' performed their craft, Mortimer chopped up bits of wood for sale as firewood and kindling, sometimes inadvertently demolishing valuable antiques or pieces left by his father for incorporating in fine furniture.

He also spent a lot of time sweeping his shop floor, and so effective was he that his shop became known as the tidiest and cleanest in Yorkshire. One reason was that it was never used.

His enterprise as the village undertaker came to an abrupt end when a local man, Jonathan Holgate, became terminally ill. Mrs Micklethwaite prepared Mortimer for the task of building the coffin by explaining what would happen when Mr Holgate did eventually pass away, but the silly Mortimer upset the family by going to the house to measure Mr Holgate while he was still alive. Some said the shock killed Mr Holgate.

And then Mortimer's own mother died. As a final act of love, Mortimer built her a coffin which would have accommodated a giant, but the vicar allowed the funeral to go ahead even if the resultant grave looked large enough to be a communal one. But Mortimer was proud of that job. Upon his mother's death, however, the problem was – what would Mortimer do now that his mother had gone? She had done her best to sustain him by helping him with the business, but she had had limited success.

Acting alone, Mortimer was incapable of running the workshop, useless at performing the necessary craftsmanship and incompetent at organizing his business and personal life. Then an answer came, as if from heaven. The village needed a postman.

The postmistress, Dorothy Porteus, put a notice in her shop window to say that her husband, Lawrence, was retiring as the delivery postman and that a new one was required.

It was a part-time post because Crampton was a small village; the job demanded some four hours work each day except Sunday, and it was a permanent position. The small wage ruled out most family men and it would not be easy filling the position; then someone suggested Mortimer. He had the time, he needed the money, he never left the village and he knew everyone. It seemed an ideal answer. He went to see Mrs Porteus and she filled in his application form, knowing the right words to use. She said she'd have a word with the head postmaster in York and would recommend Mortimer for the job. She'd remain as postmistress to issue stamps, postal orders, pensions and so forth as she continued to run her general store and newsagency, and Mortimer would deliver the mail.

And so, with the minimum of fuss, Mortimer got the job.

There was only one real problem.

Mortimer could not read.

His mother and father must have known, but Mortimer had managed his own affairs without anyone realizing that particular deficiency. When Mrs Porteus had filled in his application form, Mortimer had signed it, something he had learned to do, and thus no one in the post office had discovered his secret. It was revealed on his first morning's duty. The Ashfordly post-office van delivered a pile of letters and packets to Crampton village shop-cum-post office, as Mortimer arrived to begin the day's delivery.

His first task was to sort the letters into some kind of logical sequence for his walk around the village, and that's when Mrs Porteus realized what she'd done. But she did not want to appear a fool by admitting her error and so she told Mortimer where to deliver his first few letters, advising him to ask a householder if he reached a confusing stage.

For several blissful years, therefore, Crampton was served by a postman who could not read. Mrs Porteus would set him off with his first handful of letters, telling him which houses to visit, and then he would ask for advice at one of the houses for his next directions. The villagers soon realized the problem, but they decided never to reveal it – after all, they would look a bit silly if they told the world about Mortimer.

Through this mutual aid from the villagers, the post was always delivered; that incredibly efficient network of advisers kept Mortimer's secret and it provided him with a welcome and necessary income and occupation.

I must admit that I knew nothing of this until I went into Crampton to deliver a summons. It had been sent to me from Manchester City Police with a request that I deliver it personally to a Mr Charles Finney who lived at Snowdrop Cottage in Crampton. It was for a careless driving charge in the Manchester area, but I did not know Finney, nor did I know where to find Snowdrop Cottage. Most of the houses did not have names or did not display their names, the logic being that the villagers all knew one another.

As I drove into Crampton that morning, who should I see but Mortimer in his postman's uniform and carrying a big sack of letters. I halted my van and approached him with the address of the summons uppermost.

'Where's this house, Mortimer?' I showed him the address. 'There's no street name given.'

He peered at the typewritten address and shook his head.

'No idea, Mr Rhea. Sorry.'

'But you do know the man, surely?'

'What man, Mr Rhea?'

'This man, the man named here. Mr Finney.'

'Oh, that man! Yes, he lives in Moor Street, third house along. Used to be called Jasmine Cottage till the jasmine died ... now it's Snowdrop Cottage because the garden's full of snowdrops in February ... '

I looked at him.

'You can't read!' I realized. 'You've no idea what it says here, have you?'

He blushed and hung his head; he'd been brought up never to lie to a policeman and I could see he was acutely embarrassed.

'Does the post office know?' I put to him.

He shook his head.

'And so, for the last few years you've been delivering the mail without being able to read the addresses?'

'Aye,' he said. 'They help me if I'm stuck. I know a lot now, by the shape and colour of the envelopes ... regular stuff, you know.'

'Well, if you've managed all this time without the post office knowing, I'm not going to tell them, Mortimer.'

'Thanks, Mr Rhea. It's a good job for me, is this one.'

I smiled and nodded. 'The best,' I said, going into Moor Street to deliver my summons.

8 Currents of Domestic Joy

'Withindoors house – the shocks!'
Gerard Manley Hopkins (1844–89)

'The decorators are coming in a couple of weeks, Rhea,' Sergeant Blaketon rang at half past eight one morning to inform me. 'I'll send you the official notification – it's internal, all rooms upstairs and down, and the office. You'll be given some wallpaper sample books to make a selection from, within the official price range that is. The decorator will see you about your choice of paper and paint, but don't go mad, we don't want the police house looking like a sleazy night club, do we? But the office will be in the official colour, cream walls and woodwork. We want none of your psychedelic pinks in there.'

At this news, my heart sank. Several times during my service, Mary and I had suffered the intrusions of the official decorators, both internally and externally. They came as an army, van loads of white-overalled men who plonked huge smelly cans of paint all over the place, followed by rolls of wallpaper and paste buckets, and who ignored the domestic routine which had to continue midst the mayhem. They came at eight in the morning and covered everything with protective sheets, then left at 4.30 in the afternoon after consuming gallons of coffee or tea. This invasion lasted for about ten days, i.e. two whole weeks discounting weekends.

The internal decoration of our police houses was scheduled once in every seven years, with the external woodwork being repainted every four years. The outside work was never a real problem unless the days were very cold – the painters seemed able to work only when all doors and windows were standing open. It was the internal decorating which was more disruptive; it was worse than moving house. Some officers managed to avoid internals – by being transferred around the county and exchanging police houses on a regular, short-term basis, some had never experienced the trauma of being internally decorated. At times I wondered if they engineered their transfers simply to avoid the decorators.

But others, like me, seemed to arrive at a house weeks before the decorators were due; even though we seldom occupied our police houses for more than three years, we always contrived to be resident when they were due to be decorated internally. Once I had to tolerate the wallpaper choice of the previous tenant because he suddenly moved out after making his selection and had gone to pastures new before the decorators came to honour his and his wife's wishes. Fortunately, their choice was tolerable. Conversely, we had one of our houses decorated shortly before we moved out: our bedrooms were done in nursery rhymes and fairy-story pictures, not very welcoming for the teenage lads who followed us.

On this occasion at Aidensfield, however, things were likely to be more difficult than usual.

One problem was that we had four tiny children, and the second was that I was working shifts, including nights, which meant on occasions I'd be trying to sleep during the daytime while the painters were working. The logistics of getting the painting done in tandem with our frantic domestic routine promised more than a few headaches. I could anticipate finger-marked doors, upturned paintpots and lost tempers from all parties. Much of the aggravation would fall on poor Mary for, unless I was on nights, I would be out of the house on duty, and thus out of the way, for some eight hours of most painting days.

For me, it was a strange experience having decorators to do

the work, for I'd always been brought up to do my own painting and decorating, household maintenance, repairs of domestic machinery, fitting of tap washers, installation of wall lights and so forth. For me as a child, DIY was not a new fad – it had always been my father's mode of living and so it was with me. It was odd, therefore, watching others do what I would have normally done myself, but, in an official house, one had to abide by the rules. Even if a tap wanted something as basic as a new washer, the job had to be done by a professional engaged by the county council. What I could have done for the cost of the washer would cost the ratepayers a large amount. Nonetheless, we were allowed to decorate our own interiors within that seven years, and indeed I did so when convenient. In spite of that, seven-year internals had to be done on schedule.

The constabulary sought tenders from private contractors for this work and, because it was linked so closely to the county council, the police were compelled to accept the lowest offer. Thus quality did not enter into the bargain – the job was done on the cheap. Cheap paint, cheap paper and cheap labour was employed. When a contractor was awarded the work, it meant he usually had many other police houses to decorate as part of his contract. As a consequence, he would rush around them all to strip off the old wallpaper and check the old paintwork, then he'd tear about with undercoats, followed by gloss paint, probably decorating five or six houses at the same time.

It did take about ten days to complete one house, but those ten days were not always consecutive, sometimes being spread over a month or more. This also meant that if he said he'd come to our house on Monday, it might be Friday by the time he arrived owing to some unexpected delay, but we had, in the meantime, cleared the rooms in readiness. The disruption could be considerable and there is little wonder we never looked forward to our nice new decor.

But that was the system and we had to abide by it. Some of us grumbled; some of us said if the authorities gave us the money it cost to complete that seven-year internal, we could do the work ourselves. This was looked upon with some scepticism for one senior officer asked, 'But if we give you the money, what guarantee have we that you'll do the job?'

Such was the trust among one's fellow officers. Another suggestion was that we did the work and obtained receipts for the expenditure on materials, with inspection of our handiwork being welcomed. This was also frowned upon, one excuse being that some officers might not be very capable DIY decorators. So none of our suggestions was considered. The system would not be altered – the houses would be decorated internally every seven years by the contractor who submitted the lowest tender, and that was that.

Within a couple of days of Sergeant Blaketon's call, therefore, we received large books of sample wallpapers with a note that we had to return them the same day because they had to be circulated among several of my colleagues. We had to make a note of the reference numbers for each room and the decorator would call shortly; we had to give him those numbers and inform him for which room each paper was intended. He would inspect the rooms to determine the precise number of rolls required. The kitchen would not be wallpapered – its walls would be glossed and so would those of the bathroom/toilet upstairs and the downstairs toilet. We could wallpaper each of the three bedrooms, the lounge, the dining room and the entrance hall/staircase/landing. The cost must not exceed the stated total amount, but if we had cheap paper upstairs we could have more expensive designs in the reception rooms downstairs.

And so we laboured over those books, having to rush our selection from the somewhat limited range, but Mary and I did find some papers which met our joint approval. And there were papers for the children's bedrooms which they helped to select – nursery rhyme scenes, Disney characters and so forth. Now we awaited the visit of the decorator who had won the contract and we knew what to expect – he would try to persuade us to accept different, cheaper papers. He would highlight those of similar colour and design, and if we succumbed to his charms, he would make more profit.... We'd experienced this technique many times before and so we knew the tricks of their trade.

Shortly afterwards, I received a telephone call from a Mr Rodney Osbourne of Osbourne's Decorators, saying he'd like to call and discuss our requirements. We arranged a time when I'd be at home and, on the day in question, Mary had the kettle boiling and some home-made buns ready. We would show Mr Osbourne some hospitality at this early stage. We reckoned that would shorten pressurized discussions with him – if we were nice to him, he would respond with efficient service.

At the appointed time of eleven o'clock, a scruffy white van arrived in our drive from which a short, round man emerged. Thin strands of dark hair formed a bizarre network on his balding head; he wore rounded spectacles with heavy rims and a brown dustcoat with pens in the breast pocket. He had a clip-board in one hand and a book of wallpaper samples in the other.

I opened the front door and invited him to enter. He shook my hand and said, 'Osbourne.'

'PC Rhea,' I introduced myself. 'Nick. And this is Mary, my wife, and the children.... '

All four emerged from the lounge where they were playing and stood staring at him. He patted them on their heads and said, 'They'll be going to stay with their granny, are they? When my fellers come?'

'No,' I said. 'They'll be here.'

'I don't do this for a profit, you know,' he began. 'There's no profit in doing police houses. I just take the job on to keep my men in work and you know, when times are slack. Kids can cause delays, get in the way, you know, and I don't want delays, I can't afford delays, not on a cut-price job like this ... '

'Their grandparents are all at work,' I said. 'We can't expect them to take time off to look after our kids. Besides, they're well behaved ... '

'They all say that. I could tell you some tales about

policemen's kids ... '

'Cup of coffee, Mr Osbourne?' asked Mary quietly.

'Wouldn't say no,' he said, following her into the kitchen as I shooed the children back into the lounge. I told them to stay there until we had finished talking to the gentleman and asked Elizabeth to keep an eye on the others. Even at her tender age, she could control her brother and sisters. But their excitement was too great – they had all been told about their new bedrooms, about the new paint and wallpaper, and were anxious to see the miracle-worker who would achieve all this. Four tiny heads appeared around the kitchen door, but they remained quiet, watching him as a cat might watch a playing mouse. Mary's coffee and buns achieved their intended purpose and he said he'd tolerate the bairns if they were kept in one room while his men operated.... The more controlled the children were, the sooner his men would finish.

Then followed the anticipated 'advice' about our selection of wallpapers.

'Now for that back bedroom you'll need seven rolls of that one you've picked.' He scribbled on his pad. 'But in this book here, there's one the same colour as yours, but the pattern's smaller, which means we can use less rolls, you know, one less mebbe on a room that size ... that's a saving, you know ... it all adds up and we don't make a profit on these jobs ... '

'Then we could have more expensive paper in the lounge,' said Mary, smiling at him with all her feminine charm.

'Now I wasn't quite thinking like that,' he countered. 'I mean, there's little enough in this for us as it is, and so far as the lounge is concerned, I think this one here ... ' and he flicked to another in his book, 'is better than your choice – smaller pattern, lighter background, prettier an' all, hard wearing, you know, where the kids'll touch it ... '

'We were told not to exceed the sum allocated,' I said. 'And our choice does that, Mr Osbourne, even allowing for big repeat patterns and extra rolls ... '

'Aye, well, I was just trying to be helpful, you know, not restricting you to that first book, you understand.'

'Thanks, but we are happy with that book,' I said. 'We've made up our minds.'

'Oh, well, so long as you're happy,' and he closed the pattern book with a snap of its pages. 'Well, if you let me see the rooms, I'll work out the number of rolls … '

Having been decorated many times, the Force records contained the numbers required because all local police houses had rooms of a standard size and that had already been taken into account in allocating the contract to Mr Osbourne. But we did not object. He went round the rooms, jotting things down on his pad and making a fuss of measuring windows and doors.

'Magnolia,' he said, tapping a window ledge in the main bedroom. 'Gloss.'

'Magnolia, in here?' Mary looked at me.

'It won't go very well with our bedroom paper,' I said. 'Magnolia's a creamy off-white, isn't it? We were thinking of something that would be a better match.'

'Magnolia goes with anything, you know,' he said. 'That's why we use nowt else, gloss and matt, emulsion and paint.'

'We'd like a pinkish tint on this woodwork,' Mary tried. 'Something that's more in keeping with the new bedroom paper.'

'Put a pink bulb in your bedside lamp, Mrs Rhea – it'll give out a lovely glow, and your magnolia'll look grand. It'll pick up surrounding colours, you know – get a red sky in the morning and that magnolia'll look lovely. Blue skies make it look good, even grey skies give it charm, so they say.'

'But I don't want magnolia,' she said.

'It's in the contract.' He tapped his pad with his pencil. 'Magnolia on all interior wood surfaces. It says so in writing. It's been agreed.'

I had no way of countering that statement and winked at Mary. I said we'd accept it. Magnolia it would be – all over!

'When will you be coming?' I asked. 'I need to know so that I can clear the rooms and make them ready.'

He pulled a tattered diary from his rear pocket and flicked through it.

'Three weeks on Monday,' he said. 'Eight o'clock sharp.'

Mary did a quick calculation.

'That's the week my mum's coming to stay,' she said. 'Can you make it a week later?'

He checked his diary again. 'Right, yes. No problem, I can do a job in Eltering that week. Right. Four weeks on Monday it is.'

And off he went.

'You shouldn't have agreed to magnolia all over!' Mary grumbled afterwards. 'I'm sure we can choose colours, within the price range.'

'I know, but I'll have words with the workmen when they arrive. They'll ignore their boss – he doesn't paint any more, he just organizes things. We'll get our pink paintwork, you'll see.' I felt sure I could persuade them towards our wishes.

Mary's mum came on the Sunday evening a week before the painters were due and said she'd help to prepare the house for them. There were carpets to take up, furniture to remove, paintwork to wash down and so forth, and the painters wanted us to live in one room while they prepared and decorated all the others.

But at eight o'clock that Monday morning, the painters arrived. I was in bed, having worked half-nights until 2 a.m. A very anxious Mary knocked me up.

'They're here!' she cried. 'The painters. And mother's here, and you're in bed and they said they weren't coming till next week ... '

'Tell them to come back next week,' I groaned.

'The foreman says no, he's been told to come here now, today. They're already moving paint pots and all their stuff into your office ... '

I struggled out of bed and went down to greet the invaders. By then, they'd half-filled my office floor with tins of paint and rolls of wallpaper. I succeeded in identifying the foreman.

'We weren't expecting you. Your boss said you'd come next Monday,' I tried valiantly. 'You're a week early!'

'Well, he was wrong, mister. Our schedule says today, and

he said nowt about a change. If we miss today we'll be out of work a week and we can't afford no wages, not like you blokes with secure jobs, and if we wait till next week, you might have to wait months because we'll have to re-schedule our rota, and then Harry's going on holiday and it'll cause a right cock-up in our office and things are bad enough there as it is, what with Sandra getting pregnant and being sick every morning, and there's nobody to order the paper and paint, and the police and fire brigade all wanting houses done, and them nurses' homes.'

I began to wish I hadn't asked.

'Right, you can stay.' I decided that the sooner we got this job finished, the better. 'We'll cope. But can you do a favour for me?'

'Depends,' he said.

'We'd like delicate pink, blush pink I think they call it, on the bedroom woodwork instead of magnolia.'

'We've only got magnolia. It's magnolia in here, your office that is, and the kitchen and bathroom, glossed walls, matt emulsion wood and ceilings ... the contract says magnolia on all woodwork. I've got my orders.'

'If I get my own pink paint, could you put it on?'

'We're not allowed to use other folks' materials, but seeing as we've caused a bit of hassle, I'll see if we've any pink in our warehouse, or red. We might mix red with magnolia ... '

And so they stayed. It was chaotic. To enable them to whizz around the house with brushes flailing, and to give them a clear run in as many rooms as possible, we had to live and eat in one room. The snag was it was a different room each day. As Mary, her mother and the children huddled in one room during the day while I was out in the countryside, the painters slapped on gallons of magnolia undercoat and gloss; it would dry overnight and then they'd use the gloss. But at night, I had to move all our furniture into the room they'd just done, watchful of wet paint, because the next day, they wanted to be in the room we were using.

Like nomads, we moved about the house to allow

undercoating and moved all over again to allow the glossing and then the papering. We lodged in the office, we sat on the stairs, the children cried, our meals were either like picnics or burnt offerings, and the office, newly painted in glorious magnolia, became an overflow second home/granny annexe. The children touched wet magnolia; they got magnolia in their hair and on their clothes; they left their fingerprints on magnolia door pillars, magnolia door frames and the magnolia staircase. But, surprisingly, the house did look better – except for the downstairs toilet. Our predecessor had painted the interior walls with a very dark blue gloss paint, but these men decided that it would have to be magnolia gloss. They slapped on a coat – and the blue showed through, making it a dirty kind of sea-green. It looked like the interior of a grimy fish-tank.

'You'll be putting another coat on that loo?' I said.

'No, only one coat of gloss,' said the foreman. 'That's the rule.'

'But it looks awful!' I grumbled.

'Some folks are never satisfied!' he said. 'Free decorating and still they're not pleased. By gum, I don't know what the world's coming to! Craftsman-decorated loos … they'll be asking for hand-carved toilet seats next … '

I gave up. I'd paint it myself when they'd gone because it was too ghastly for any of our visitors. It could put them off the purpose for which they resorted to this little room. The last room to be done was the main bedroom, partly because I was on night duty on that final Thursday and Friday.

I'd be out of the house from 10 p.m. until 6 a.m. While they were completing the decoration of my usual bedroom, I would sleep during the day in the tiny back room with its Snow White and Seven Dwarfs paper. In spite of our reservations, the two weeks had flown and the house was looking much better, even if it did smell of new paint and in spite of having to cope with mother-in-law and four children. In fact, she was an enormous help in keeping them occupied, taking them for walks and helping to organize the ritual shifting of furniture every night while poor Mary coped with all the other domestic chores.

And so, on that final Friday morning, I returned from my tour of duty at 6 a.m., had a light snack and climbed thankfully into bed.

The decorators would be here at eight and I would rise around 2 p.m. or so. As I climbed into my warm bed in the back room, Mary and the children were in our marital bed, with mother-in-law in the middle room, and I did not disturb them. Mary, the children and her mum would get up early to ensure everything was ready for the men to finish their work today and, by tonight, the house would be ours again. It would be smart and clean, fresh and new, albeit smelling of paint.

But I must have been shattered because I overslept. During the day, I'd been vaguely aware of movements on the stairs, of painters working and children trying to be quiet. Those disruptions and my night without sleep had conspired to keep me in bed until five o'clock. I woke in the knowledge that I was on nights again at 10 p.m. that night, but would cope easily after my restful sleep. But now the house was quiet. I peeped out of the bedroom window and saw that the decorators' van had gone, as had their ladders and other equipment. I smiled as I walked to the bathroom, but decided to inspect our lovely new bedroom.

It was covered with magnolia paint.

It looked awful against the colour scheme we had selected and I groaned. With officialdom, the little man can never win. I'd do it myself within a week or two ... when I had time. As I sat down to my evening meal with the scent of new paint all about me, I said to Mary,

'Darling, promise me one thing.'

'What's that?'

'When we get a house of our own, promise you'll never grow magnolia in the garden, that we'll never buy a house called Magnolia House and we'll never use magnolia paint in any of our colour schemes.'

'Oh, I don't know,' she smiled. 'I quite like it, now it's on.'

* * *

Being the wife of a policeman is never easy. There are the pressures of a unique kind of work, with the added menace of danger, and there are the unsocial hours that must be tolerated. If a policeman's tour of duty is scheduled to end at a given time and then, minutes before he is due to finish work some urgent task crops up, then he must attend to it. Unlike so many jobs, we cannot walk away from work when the hooter sounds. And, fortunately, police officers do maintain a sense of responsibility towards the public and will continue to work when needed.

This means that many officers work very long hours, especially those who serve in the CID: they can't cease their inquiries just because it's five o'clock and time to go home. Happily, many police wives understand this necessary commitment, and Mary was one of them. She knew that I had a responsibility to the public whom I served even if, at times, this did mean sacrificing a normal social life. It was very difficult to make definite plans for anything.

Even when I was off duty, in the evenings or at weekends, or perhaps having friends in for a meal, the public was not to know this, and if people came to the house I had to deal with them. If a man knocked on the door while I was enjoying time off and said he'd just been involved in a traffic accident in the village, then I couldn't ignore him.

It was a similar story even when I was not at home. If I was out on patrol, the police house remained a police house. Its continuing role was announced by its blue POLICE sign in front of the adjoining office and noticeboard. So when people wanted help, they would come to the house even if the sole occupant was a young, untrained woman with four tiny children. And, like me, Mary could not ignore anyone with a genuine, urgent problem. In such cases, she was always a tower of strength, always operating as my devoted unpaid assistant. From time to time, while I was away on duty, she'd coped with callers in trouble – like a woman who complained of rape, a man who had found a house on fire and a dead man inside, a lorry driver who had run off the road, victims of petty crime and all manner of other routine chores. In all cases, she'd coped with calmness and efficiency.

But the wife of a country policeman receives no pay or reward for her supportive work, save that her efforts are appreciated, coupled with the knowledge that the public hold her in high regard.

It follows that there were times when it was difficult for both Mary and I ever to be free from such responsibility. The only way to avoid continuous duty was to get away from the house altogether during my leisure hours. Mary and I therefore did our best to take time away from home during my days off, even when those days off occurred mid-week. I was always aware of the difficulties this caused, particularly when the children started school, and Mary's tolerance meant that I endeavoured to compensate her whenever I could. In spite of the demands on us, I liked her to go out alone, to get involved with village events, to drive into town or to have a life of her own.

I was delighted, therefore, when she was asked by the ladies of Aidensfield WI to attend one of their monthly meetings and talk about her life as the wife of a village policeman. I knew she would do a good job, even if she felt some reservation about speaking in public, and I persuaded her to accept the challenge. When the secretary suggested a date, I checked with my advance duty roster and found I was scheduled to perform duty from 10 a.m. until 6 p.m. on that day. Mary's talk was to begin at 7.30 p.m. in the village hall and so I could return home in time to baby-sit. The meeting was still two months away and so I could ensure I'd be off duty; if my duties were re-scheduled, I could ask a colleague to swap shifts if necessary. But my duties were not tampered with and Mary's big day arrived.

'You'll be sure to finish on time?' Mary requested as I prepared to leave home that morning.

'I've nothing pressing today,' I assured her. 'I'll be home at six.'

'But sometimes we've had to cancel things, dances, dinners and so on, when you've had to stay on to deal with a sudden death or an accident or something ... '

'There'll be other men on duty this evening,' I said. 'If something happens last minute, I'm sure I can get somebody to take over from me.'

The fear of some unexpected occurrence was always present on such occasions and I could understand Mary's concern: we'd had to cancel so many outings because of last-minute changes to my duty or through last minute official dramas ...

But that day, I set off with confidence, manoeuvring my little van onto the road. My first job was to visit the Section Office in Ashfordly to collect any waiting correspondence, and then I would drive to Crampton and Gelderslack to deal with several applications for renewals of firearm certificates. It was going to be a gentle routine day of non-urgent duties.

And so it was – until quarter to five.

My official radio crackled into action as I was ordered to attend a traffic accident on the road between Ashfordly and Brantsford. Initial reports suggested that a van had emerged from a side road directly into the path of a fast-moving car.

I groaned.

'Ten four,' I acknowledged. 'Will attend. Any report of casualties?'

'Negative,' said Control. 'It is a minor accident. A breakdown vehicle has been called and is en route. What is your ETA?'

'16.55,' I said, calculating that it was a ten-minute run from my present location at Crampton.

When I arrived at the scene, I found a small grey van in the ditch and a Ford Cortina on its side nearby. The two drivers were waiting, their anger long spent, and neither was injured. It seemed the van driver was at fault, thinking he'd had the time to emerge from a side road ahead of the oncoming car, when in fact he had not. The car driver had taken swift evasive action, but in spite of his efforts, had collided with the front nearside of the van, spinning it around and hurtling it off the highway. Neither man was hurt but each of their vehicles was badly damaged.

I obtained details including a statement from each, and decided that consideration would have to be given to prosecution of the van driver for careless driving. I told him in the formal jargon of the Notice of Intended Prosecution and was pleased when the breakdown truck arrived. It lifted the car onto the rear platform and hoisted the van onto its front wheels, then departed with both. The drivers went too. They would make their own arrangements to get home.

The immediate necessities of the incident were over; my typing of the report, my production of a scale plan of the scene and my preparation of the case papers could wait until tomorrow. It was now five minutes to six – I'd be a few minutes late booking off duty, but at least the job had been completed in good time. Mary would get her night out. I radioed Control to up-date them on the outcome of the accident and reported that the matter had been dealt with. I concluded by saying I was en route to Aidensfield to book off duty.

I'd only covered three miles when the radio burbled into action once again. This time it was urgent.

'Control to All Mobiles in Ashfordly/Brantsford/Eltering district. Urgent. All mobiles and foot patrols to rendezvous at Ashfordly Police Office immediately,' was the instruction. 'Await further orders there. Acknowledge. Over.'

I groaned aloud. I couldn't believe it! My heart sank as I wondered what on earth had happened, but I did recognize that the voice of the Control Room operator carried a note of real urgency. I responded by giving my call-sign and saying I was en route and would arrive within ten minutes. Mary's night out was in jeopardy once again but I could not intrude on the airwaves to ask what it was all about. I'd be blocking valuable transmissions. I would have to wait to find out more when I arrived at Ashfordly. I turned the van around and hurtled through the lanes.

When I arrived at the police station, other cars were assembling and Sergeant Blaketon was jotting down the names of those who had arrived.

'What's happened?' I asked Alwyn Foxton, the duty constable at Ashfordly.

'Two men raided the pub at Stovingsby,' he said. 'After hours. Not long ago in fact. They got in through the back door, tied up the licensee and his wife and got away with cash and jewellery. They crashed their car into a tractor while escaping – their car's a write-off and they've taken to the moors on foot. We're the search party. We're assembling here. The dog section's been called out. Once we're all here, we'll get our orders.'

My dismay must have been evident. I thought of poor Mary.

'Where were these characters last seen?' I asked.

'Heading across the moor towards Gelderslack. On foot,' he said. 'We've got other cars coming in from the north and traffic division's establishing road blocks, but finding those two won't be easy. The dogs might catch them,' he added.

'Have I time to ring Mary?' I asked, wondering if there was a free telephone.

'Sure, there's a few more of us to come before we get briefed. Use the one in my house,' he offered, for his house was next to Ashfordly Police Station. Mary was not at all pleased.

'But you said you'd definitely be home.' I could hear the disappointment in her voice. 'And I promised those ladies that I'd go ... I can't let them down. How long will you be?'

'I don't know.' I couldn't offer any indication of a home-coming time, but added, 'I might be away all night, it depends.'

'What can I do then?' There was a note of desperation in her voice.

'Try Mrs Quarry,' I suggested. 'Surely she'll baby-sit at short notice, if she knows the reason ... '

'But we put on her far too much, she's so good.'

'I'm sorry, darling.' Through Alwyn's window I could see Sergeant Blaketon calling everyone indoors. 'I must go, we're assembling for our briefing now. And good luck with the talk.'

She didn't reply as she put down the telephone and I knew she must be both angry and upset, but what could I do? I just hoped that Mrs Quarry was able to baby-sit. I had no way of keeping in touch with Mary as I received my briefing for the search. From the information received, the two men had broken cover to run into the hills above Lairsbeck, heading for the forests and open moors of Lairsdale. A farmer had seen them running and had called Eltering Police, and so one dog unit, two cars and eight officers had been directed there instead of attending our briefing. They would maintain contact. The hunt was on, and with the aid of radios and police dogs, we felt sure we would trace and capture the villains.

My brief was to patrol the higher points of Lairsdale, touring the isolated farms and cottages in that remote, widespread community to warn the widely scattered residents of the fleeing robbers and to record any possible sightings. It was seven o'clock when I left the office armed with a list of names taken from the electoral register and a map showing the position of remote farms and cottages in the higher reaches of Lairsdale. I wondered how Mary was getting on, but our official radios could not be used for contacting home. Although we had a radio on our official vehicles, the rural constables did not have official radios in their offices. Sometimes, if we were engaged in anything exciting, our wives would listen on our own portable radios – coded messages might sometimes be transmitted!

Mary would sometimes listen to my voice at work by tuning in to the police wavelength. Lots of people used this technique, including journalists, and so they could listen to a very one-sided commentary as we went about our more exciting duties. There was nothing illegal in listening – it became illegal if anyone, other than the police, acted on the information thus acquired. But Mary would not be listening tonight – hopefully, she'd be entertaining the WI members. I raced into the hills, anxious to get this job finished as soon as possible – I was hungry too, having been dragged away from any chance of having my evening meal on time! The sooner we got this job over, the sooner I would eat.

As I motored high into the dale with my radio burbling constantly, I saw a lonely roadside telephone kiosk. I'd ring Mary from here. But when I got through, Mrs Quarry answered.

'She's gone,' I was told. 'Not five minutes ago. Your supper's in the oven for when you get back.... How long will you be, Mr Rhea?'

'I don't know,' I had to say. 'But thanks for stepping in at short notice.'

'She said she should be back by ten,' Mrs Quarry told me.

'I might be in before then.' I was hopeful of an early finish. 'Or I might be later. I'm heading for Lairsbeck – we're hunting two robbers,' I added for dramatic effect.

'It was on the news,' she told me. 'But watch out and be careful.'

'I will,' I assured her.

'Don't forget to search Low Holly Heads while you're up there,' she added.

'Why, what's at Low Holly Heads?'

'Nowt,' she answered. 'It's a ruin now. My grandfather used to farm there years ago, for the estate. It's not far from the track that goes over those heights, though. A good hiding spot, I'd say, especially if those chaps are heading that way like the radio said they were.'

'Thanks, I'll check it out.' I was pleased to be provided with this piece of local information. All I had was a list of occupied farms, not ruins.

I'd bear it in mind, and a glance at my map showed it was close to my intended tour of the occupied premises. My initial visits produced no information; none of the farmers or cottagers had seen the runaways but at least they now knew of our interest and promised they'd contact us if the men did appear. By the time I'd visited all those outlying places, it was almost 8.30; darkness would fall around nine and if the men had not been traced, they might go to ground for the night. From reports over my official radio, I knew there had been no more sightings in other areas and our dogs had lost the trail near a stream. I decided it was now time to look at Low Holly Heads. I could take the van to within some three-quarters of a mile of the ruined farm, the final stretch of the old road being impassable to cars now. And so, as darkness began to fall, I walked down the track.

It led through a steep field, across a stream in the gulley below, and then climbed up the far side through a pine wood. The old farm lay on the slopes above that wood. I could see it in the distance, a stark stone-built house with most of its roof missing and its walls tumbling down. But parts were tiled and it did offer some shelter. As I hurried down the steep track, I heard voices and then a shout – they'd seen me! Two men were running away from the farm, climbing higher along the steep hillside. I'd be quarter of a mile away from them ... should I chase them, or call for help?

If I chased them on foot, I'd lose them, of that there was little doubt in this rough, expansive terrain, and so I ran back to the van, waited a moment to gain my breath and then reported to Control. I explained the difficulties due to the rough nature of the landscape, the lack of tracks, the steep hillsides leading to open moorland, the acres of heather and bracken, the gulleys and streams. Dogs would be needed, lighting would have to be available, a field radio system would be an asset – this was before the advent of personal radios for police officers.

I was told to wait at my van and to rendezvous there with the members of search party as they arrived. Two units of dog handlers had been despatched and the dogs would be put on the trail, consequently no one must interfere with the scent which led from Low Holly Heads. I confirmed that I had not trampled upon the men's tracks and this pleased Blaketon: so many villains have escaped due to police officers confusing the dogs by trampling all over the fresh scent trails.

I looked at my watch. It was nine o'clock. The sun had set and darkness was beginning to envelope the dramatic landscape as I wondered how Mary was faring with her talk. She should have finished by now. My radio was in constant action by this time, asking me for updates, for directions to the scene and for a recommendation as to the use of specialist vehicles, like a four-wheel drive truck which could be borrowed from the mountain rescue service.

Was there any track for such a vehicle to use? My own knowledge of the area combined with judicious use of the Ordnance Survey map suggesting the fleeing men would quickly reach the bridleway which formed a northern boundary to Lairsdale Moor; the track formed a semi-circle around the bulk of the rising moor and led to both east and west. It was used by Forestry Commission vehicles, ramblers and horse riders. I suggested that units be despatched to each end of that bridleway....

Within half an hour, Sergeant Blaketon arrived, rapidly followed by a mass of other police vehicles and officers, some of whom had been called out an hour early to begin their night duty. They'd started at nine o'clock instead of ten – I wondered how many of those had missed their suppers! The inspector had been dragged away from his and had opted to operate from the western end of the bridleway, taking with him several more officers. And so a huge search was mounted. Blaketon despatched two units of dog handlers to Low Holly Heads Farm where they succeeded in picking up the trail. Off they went, noses following the scent like bloodhounds, while I remained with my van and its radio, acting as co-ordinator for this end of the search because of my knowledge of the terrain.

It was a dog handler who caught the men. Having fled at the distant sight of me trekking towards their hiding place in Low Holly Heads, they had crossed the open moor to find shelter in an old sheepshed.

The absence of officers in hot pursuit had convinced the men they had evaded us and so they had settled down, whereas in fact we had been consolidating our search. The triumphant dog handler and his happy Alsatian escorted the captives back to their vehicle and so to Eltering Police Station. And they were still in possession of the stolen property; their guilt would never be in question.

It was 10.30 when I returned to Ashfordly Police Station to record my part in the search, and quarter past eleven by the time I arrived home. Mary was back, I was pleased to say. I kissed her and said I'd be with her in just a few moments, when I had taken off my uniform and booked off duty. I knew she had rustled up a fresh meal for me – I knew that the moment I walked in from the scent of cooking which wafted from the kitchen. I then realized how famished I was. Now (hopefully) finished for the day, I put on my slippers and settled down to ask Mary about her evening. I found that, in spite of the late hour, she had set the table in the dining room; there was a candle in the middle and a bottle of wine already opened....

'Hey!' I was very pleasantly surprised. 'What's all this for?'

'They gave me a bottle of wine for talking to them, and, well, I thought I'd been unreasonable with you earlier, you know, getting cross with you when you're only doing your job ... so I did this, for both of us.'

I kissed her and cuddled her warmly, thanking her for this generous thought, and then we settled down to the meal. I asked how she had coped at the WI meeting. She smiled.

'Great!' she beamed. 'I took our portable radio.... I told them about the demands on us both, on you especially, not knowing what was going to happen next, and then we listened to that manhunt on the radio. I used it as an example of the things you get involved in, switching it on and off every so often to illustrate points. We could only hear one side of the broadcasts, but we did hear your name mentioned several times, especially just after you'd seen those men and were co-ordinating the chase ... the ladies loved it.... '

'What a brilliant idea!' I congratulated her and we discussed our respective evenings as we enjoyed that romantic and very welcome meal. But as we were just finishing the coffee, the telephone rang. Mary looked at me and I looked at her. I groaned and said, 'Oh, not again!'

Mary said, 'I'll answer it. I'll say you're still out … '

She went into the office to take the call and returned moments later.

'It was just Mrs Quarry,' she laughed. 'She wanted to know if you'd got back safely and if you'd searched Low Holly Heads Farm like she told you to.'

'What did you say?'

'I told her you had. I said you'd pop in to thank her and tell her all about it sometime. I said you'd caught the two men who had been there … '

'It's been a very successful night.' I felt content now.

'It's not over yet,' she said, taking my hand and leading me upstairs. I hoped the telephone wouldn't ring now.

9   *Brotherly Feuds*

Peter and Paul were brothers. Peter was the elder at forty-nine years of age, while Paul was two years younger. Both lived in Crampton and were neighbours, each boasting a fine detached house in the upper part of the village, not far from the church. Their homes had extensive views over the dale to the north and east, with open fields to the south; the ancient church with its fine tower blocked their view to the west. Both had nice wives and two children, a son and daughter each. Peter's wife was called Emma and Paul's was called Sandra.

Their surname was Almsgill, their father being Percy Almsgill, then in his mid-seventies. Percy also lived in Crampton, albeit in a pleasant bungalow whose lawns reached down to the banks of a stream which flowed into the gently moving river. He and Mrs Almsgill had handed over the family firm to their sons some ten years ago, hopefully to enjoy a peaceful retirement. They were keen gardeners and, having made a success of their building business, now had the wealth and the time to make their garden a showpiece.

P. Almsgill and Sons had been a prosperous and thriving local building firm, but some eight years ago the two brothers, each called P. Almsgill, had fallen out. Peter and Paul had had an almighty row.

No one knew the reason for the dispute, although the villagers had their own ideas, some based on rumour and some on speculation. It is doubtful whether anyone knew the truth. The rumours and speculation included tales that Peter had been found in bed with Paul's wife; that Paul had been found in bed with Peter's wife; that Paul had been fiddling money from the business; that Peter had been fiddling money from the business; that Peter worked hard while Paul spent his time socializing; that Paul had made a disastrous deal which had cost the firm lots of money and that Peter had invested the firm's profits in stocks and shares that had failed. But all these and sundry other notions were unproven – there might have been a little piece of truth in every tale, or they might all have been totally false. No one really knew.

Whatever the cause of their split, the two brothers each decided that they would continue with their building business and so there were two builders in Crampton, each still known as P. Almsgill and Sons. Each claimed theirs was the original P. Almsgill and Sons and neither would change the name of their business. They even continued to share the same yard. Old Mr Percy had acquired some derelict farm buildings years ago and had converted them into a very useful builders' yard. Here were his piles of stones and tiles, roof timbers and doors, kitchen sinks, bathroom suites and toilets, some under cover and some in the open air. He also acted as a builders' merchant, selling items to customers who called.

But in their feud, the brothers had agreed to use separate parts of the yard, although they did share a common entrance. Each had an office in what had once been pigsties, and each had his own stocks of commodities and equipment.

How the postman and those who came seeking work found the right P. Almsgill remains a mystery, although everyone suspected that it was the two wives who sorted out the mess. Somehow, the right bills reached the right office and the right orders arrived upon the right desk.

There was little doubt that Emma and Sandra were responsible for keeping sanity in the yard and helping to sort out problems that would otherwise be intractable. Two charming and lovely women, they had not fallen out and there is every reason to believe they regarded their husbands' behaviour as childish. The wives remained good friends and each acted as secretary to her husband's firm, dealing with representatives, taking orders, arranging deliveries to their premises and sites currently in work and generally retaining sanity among the work force, the villagers and the customers.

The older and original P. Almsgill, i.e. Percy, kept out of this altogether – his view was that he had retired and if those b— stupid sons of his were daft enough to throw away their prospects by dividing the business, then it was their loss, not his. And he and his wife remained on good terms with both sons and their wives.

In time, the village had grown to accept this nonsense. Somehow, most of the villagers knew whether to deal with Peter or Paul on any given matter – they went to Peter if they wanted a house built and to Paul if they wanted a cowshed. They asked Peter to fix the tiles of their roofs and Paul to lay a new drive. Peter would build a conventional cemented wall around a garden while Paul would construct a drystone wall around a field or paddock. Somehow, the local people created their own demarcation lines and so the two builders found themselves specializing in certain types of work – Peter did domestic work while Paul seemed to deal with agricultural matters.

Outwardly, therefore, the two businesses appeared to thrive in a peaceful manner; certainly, the two sets of workers co-operated with each other, sometimes helping one another when the occasion demanded. I'd seen Peter's workers helping Paul's to finish a new stable block before the onset of one winter, but was later to learn that this had arisen due to the common-sense attitude of the respective wives. The brothers had known little of that deal.

As the village constable, this kind of dispute was no real concern of mine. I was aware of the problem, even if I did not know or understand the root cause, but such family matters were of no professional interest to me unless, of course, they resulted in trouble of the kind that might bring the matter into the realms of a breach of the peace.

From the outbreak of the feud, there had been no such bother, the brothers managing to contain their problems within their own bounds, but for some unaccountable reason, the underlying cause of the feud suddenly resurrected itself. No one outside the family knew why this had happened or what had prompted the sudden eruption of feeling, but the first I knew was when someone dumped a lorry load of sand in the middle of a road in Crampton. It was right outside Peter Almsgill's house.

I was told by a gamekeeper who lived nearby.

'Mr Rhea,' he halted me as I drove towards the village. 'Some daft bat's dumped a load of sand near the church. It's blocking Church Lane. I thought I'd better tell you.'

'Right, I'll see to it,' I promised.

As the mound of sand was outside Peter's home, I went to the door to ask if anyone knew about it. The house was deserted so I went to the builders' yard and found Mrs Emma.

'Sand?' She was puzzled. 'We're not expecting any sand, Mr Rhea.'

'Well, it's blocking the road outside your house,' I told her. 'And it's blocking your drive.'

She groaned.

'I bet it's Paul,' she sighed.

'Paul?' I asked.

'They're at it again, Peter and Paul,' she told me with some resignation. 'I don't know what's set them off, but they've started to play stupid tricks on each other again.'

'I'll have words with Sandra,' I offered.

Sandra was in her office at the other side of the yard and nodded. 'It'll be our Paul, wanting to annoy Peter,' she said. 'I'll get our men to shift it, Mr Rhea, straight away, with a JCB.'

'Thanks,' I said. 'And tell Paul that if he does it again, I'll book him for obstructing the highway!'

'I wish somebody would bang their heads together, Mr Rhea. Can you do that?'

'They'd have me up for assault!' I laughed.

That episode marked the beginning of a series of ridiculous nuisances which were perpetrated by some unknown persons, but we all knew it was the work of one brother against the other. Unwanted logs were dumped in their drives; shoals of unwanted mail arrived; delivery men turned up with unwanted and unordered goods like tons of liquid cement, coffins, greenhouses and paving stones. Somebody sent Paul five dogs from the dogs' home; someone else sent Peter a load of useless furniture from an auctioneer's store; Paul was sent to measure a site for a pigsty and it turned out to be at a ladies' fashion shop in Ashfordly, while Peter was asked to begin negotiations for a new house: when he went to inspect the site, it was a village pond. And so the catalogue of fun continued, with Peter playing the bagpipes outside Paul's house at six in the morning and Paul buying a pet peacock which cried all night and day in its paddock next to Peter's bedroom.

Eventually, some of the villagers did complain because these silly pranks caused them annoyance – the peacocks got out and invaded all corners of the village, stealing hen food and calling incessantly to the distraction of people living nearby; Peter's bagpipe music, which he claimed was legitimate practice for his musical tastes, was disruptive and upset the vicar, while some of the bizarre range of dumped goods did cause blockages and obstruction to footpaths and lanes. A lorry load of surplus tiger dung from the local zoo was not welcomed, nor was a dumped cartful of raw slaughter-house waste considered suitable manure for Peter's garden. I warned the brothers from time to time, always avoiding a prosecution where possible by asking them to clear away their mess – which they always did.

Then, one day, I found Paul shovelling a heap of horse manure from his drive, throwing it into a lorry which stood nearby.

'Another prank?' I asked.

'That bloody daft brother of mine,' was all he said.

'What set all this off?' I asked.

'He sent me a bill for his bloody newspapers!' Paul said. 'I wouldn't have minded, but it was more than mine. He was trying to get me to pay his paper bills!'

'How much more?' I put to him.

'Ten bob,' he said.

'In a month?' (That was the equivalent of 50 pence today.) I added, 'It was probably a mistake.'

'Never. There's never been a mistake before!'

'Who sent it to you?' I decided to get to the bottom of this now that he was talking; it was the first time I'd heard him talk of the feud.

'It was delivered,' he said. 'By hand. It always comes by hand, but I reckon he swopped them.... Why should I get his bills, eh?'

'You know Laurie Porteus has retired, don't you?' I put to him.

'So what?'

'Well, poor old Mortimer's delivering the post now, and he can't read. Now, just suppose he slipped the wrong bill through your letter box, and Peter got yours ... it could have happened. Have you asked anybody? Peter? Emma? Mrs Porteus? Mortimer?'

He hadn't asked. I don't know whether that error had been caused by Mortimer's mistaken delivery, but Paul did shrink a little at my suggestion and then went indoors.

I didn't see him for a long time afterwards, but the series of pranks ended. Even so, the feud continued and still now, there are two building firms in Crampton, each called P. Almsgill and Sons. Old Mr Percy has passed on, but Peter's son, Percy, has since joined his father's business, and so has Paul's son, also called Percy. The confusion continues.

*　　*　　*

But the brothers Almsgill were not the only ones to create a mystery for me. If local gossip and innuendo was to be believed, it was the brothers of the local Freemasons' lodge whose treatment of one of their brethren, if it was true, gave cause for concern.

Due to the mystique surrounding the rituals and rules of

Antient Fraternity of Free and Accepted Masons under the
United Grand Lodge of England, there is bound to be a lot of
unjust and unsubstantiated rumour about them and their
brotherhood. Not being a Freemason, I am not in a position to
confirm or deny any of that speculation, nor am I in a position
to criticize or praise the brotherhood. I do not know the scope
of their work, but I understand that they do perform many
acts of charity, particularly towards their own brethren and
their widows or families. That work is done through their
Board of Benevolence. Their desirable good and humane
qualities are encompassed within the Antient Charges and
Regulations which are read to the Master Elect prior to his
installation.

Similar charges of behaviour apply to members of lodges
while at their meetings or elsewhere – for example, any
Freemason must agree to be a good man who strictly obeys the
moral law. He must be a peaceable subject and cheerfully
conform to the laws of the country in which he resides. He
must promote the general good of society and cultivate the
social values, guarding against intemperance and excess. He
must work honestly and live creditably.

He must view the errors of mankind with compassion and
strive by the purity of his own conduct to demonstrate the
superior excellence of the faith he professes. And, like all
Freemasons, he may enjoy himself with innocent mirth and
avoid all excesses, always saluting his brothers in the
courteous manner in which all masons are instructed. And, in
the presence of strangers, he is told that 'You shall be cautious
in your words and carriage, that the most penetrating stranger
shall not be able to discover or find out what is not proper to
be intimated.' Hence the secrecy of the handshakes and other
salutes, and the mystique which surrounds the brotherhood.

In the course of my work, I did come across Freemasons,
because several officers, both senior and junior, were members
and so were many of the local businessmen who lived and
worked within my compass. The introductory handshake,
with the thumb pressed into the back of the recipient's hand,

is their way of finding out whether a stranger is a member – a lot of police officers who are not members recognize that handshake and return it, just to see what happens next.

Some outsiders regard the Freemasons as a harmless and curious club for men, while others see it as something sinister because of its rituals, its secrecy and the wearing of specified jewels, aprons, chains, collars, garter-blue or red silk gauntlets and other regalia.

Knowing of the high standard of behaviour required, and of their acknowledged benevolence towards their brothers, I was surprised to hear of the ill-treatment of one of them.

Maybe stories of this suppposed treatment were inaccurate, or maybe the treatment was justified. I do not know, but I can only relate the story as it appeared to me, an outsider.

The gentleman concerned was called Clarence Denby and he owned a thriving music shop in Eltering. For a small North Yorkshire market town, it was a superb shop, selling everything from pop music to the classics by way of sheet music, records, books about music and musicians, instruments and portraits of artistes and composers. Clarence's shop was popular with young and old alike for he was knowledgeable about all aspects of his art and could talk pop with teenagers just as he revealed a remarkably deep knowledge of the classics, including opera and ballet.

Clarence did not live above the shop, however. He owned a very pretty cottage beside the stream in Elsinby and he shared it with his mother. Mr Denby, senior, had died many years ago, leaving what was then a young widow with a small boy. Mother and son had lived together ever since, even though Clarence was, at the time of this story, getting on for fifty years of age. His mother was still alive and approaching her eighties, and still caring for her son. She washed his clothes, cleaned the house and prepared his meals.

Clarence had never married, but in its wisdom, nature had not made him very attractive to the opposite sex, or even to his own sex. In short, Clarence Denby was not a very pleasant man. Despite his musical knowledge and his expertise at running his business, and despite the business rapport he enjoyed with his customers, he was without any close friends.

For one thing, his appearance and general demeanour militated against him. He was a short, very fat man, barely five feet tall, who perspired persistently and heavily. On a hot day, this made the atmosphere in his tiny shop somewhat pungent and the townspeople often asked one another whether Clarence ever bathed. No one asked him directly – if they did make remarks about the midden-like atmosphere which wafted among the quavers and crotchets, they'd ask if he had a dead rat under the counter or whether someone's dog had either died or had an unfortunate accident among his LPs. Clarence's only response was to allow the shop door to stand open in high summer. His ill-fitting clothes were always shabby and greasy too – his enormous rounded belly required him to wear braces upon his trousers, and he wore a belt as well, but it appeared to be a useless girdle about his huge stomach. The belt had no known purpose, while his jacket was never fastened. Customers were greeted by a massive expanse of grubby white shirt which was eternally bursting at the buttons, a soup-stained tie with a loose knot, and acres of dark, greasy material which comprised his jacket and trousers.

Clarence's face, often described as pudgy, matched his overall appearance. It was round and fat with a multiplicity of chins, giving his eyes a distinctly piggy appearance. He wore tiny steel-rimmed spectacles which perched on the end of his bulbous nose, while his dark, greasy hair was sparse upon his balding dome, but thick about the ears and back of the neck. To add insult to injury, he had a very high-pitched voice and a peculiar wart to the left of his main chin.

In spite of all these unavoidable handicaps, Clarence's shop was popular, if only for the quality of his musical wares and his own superb knowledge. That he was an expert in musical history was never in doubt, but it seemed he did not play any instrument – at least, no one had seen or heard him in action.

In the shop, he had a middle-aged woman assistant called Peggy who tended the counter while he looked after his books during busy times, and, in local terms, it seemed that Clarence was a success. His shop was always well stocked and always busy with customers, and this aura of success was confirmed when he became a member of the Freemasons.

I would sometimes see him pottering along to meetings in Eltering, carrying his little bag of regalia, and would pass the time of day with him. He never paused for long, for he always seemed to be anxious to go about whatever business it was in which he was currently engaged. Sometimes I wondered whether he was afraid of policemen, perhaps because his mother had threatened to call one whenever he was a naughty boy.

Then, nasty rumours began to circulate about Clarence. I was never sure how the stories began, but because he lived on my beat, they did concern me. It was said that Clarence was interfering with small boys. It was claimed that part of his reason for stocking the latest pop music was to encourage young boys to visit his shop and to go upstairs to a private room to listen with Clarence.

As police officers, we were all interested to know whether or not there was any substance to these reports, but in spite of maintaining very discreet observations in and around the shop in Eltering, we could never produce any real evidence of this behaviour. I kept an eye open at Elsinby, looking out for Clarence bringing young boys home or taking them for rides in his car, but I never saw anything that would cause me to be suspicious. He was also a keen supporter of the Anglican church in Elsinby, acting as church warden and being a member of the Parochial Church Council, and so I kept an eye on his behaviour with choirboys. But, again, I saw nothing that would give rise to concern.

Not once did we receive any complaint from the parents of small boys about his behaviour, and yet, in spite of our absence of evidence and the lack of any complaint, the rumours persisted. All of us, including the CID, tried to pin down the stories; we tried to ascertain whether or not there was any substance to the tales, but found absolutely nothing.

So far as we were concerned, Clarence was not harming the children, but the public continued with their innuendoes and veiled allegations against him. I do know that we were criticized for not prosecuting him, but for what? Unlike the public, we had undertaken observations and a very comprehensive investigation into his behaviour without finding any cause for concern. We could not proceed against a man on the strength of unsupported rumours.

I do not know whether Clarence knew of these scurrilous tales, but his business did not seem to suffer. People still patronized his premises and bought his musical offerings. And then, one night, someone broke into the shop.

The broken glass of the door was discovered by one of our night patrols and the constable rang me, asking if I would rouse Clarence and ask him to come to the shop. This was the procedure we adopted for informing keyholders of breaks into their premises; we preferred the personal touch rather than a cold phone call in the dead of night. It was 6.30 that morning when I called at his house; he was at home and answered my knock. I gave him the bad news and he said he would go immediately. His presence was needed so that the constable who'd discovered the break-in could tour the shop and determine if anything had been stolen.

Having been aroused early, I made a tour of my beat before going home for breakfast but I did not see Clarence until that evening when he came home from the shop.

'Hello, Clarence.' I was in Elsinby when he turned his Morris into the drive of his house. 'What was the outcome of this morning's alarm? Anything stolen?'

He shook his fat head. 'Nothing, Mr Rhea. The door's glass panel was smashed through. I think your people are recording it as malicious damage, not shopbreaking.'

'You've not been upsetting anyone, have you?' I put to him. 'Someone having a go at your shop out of revenge?'

He shrugged his shoulders. 'No, not that I know of.' He was open with me as he added in his high-pitched voice, 'I thought it might have been kids, hard-up teenagers pinching current hits, but none's been taken. It could be damage – it might even be an accident, Mr Rhea. You know the sort of thing. Some couple courting in my shop doorway and one of them puts an elbow through the glass.'

'You could be right. Well, we'll keep our ears and eyes open, Clarence, and if you hear anything from your customers that might explain who did it and why, give us a call. We'd like to get the matter cleared up.'

'Yes, of course, Mr Rhea,' and he vanished indoors to a hot meal lovingly prepared by his aged mother.

A couple of days later, I was talking to the constable who had discovered the smashed glass and discussed it with him.

'It wasn't an accident,' he told me. 'That glass was smashed near the lock, and when I got there, the lock had opened and the door was standing ajar. It's a Yale, chummy had reached inside the broken door to release it.'

'But Clarence says nothing was stolen?' I put to him.

'I saw no signs of larceny,' he admitted. 'The till hadn't been touched and, so far as I could see, none of the stocks of records had been touched. I wouldn't know about instruments – some of those guitars, for example, are worth a lot. But Clarence reckons nothing was touched.'

'And you? What's your gut feeling?'

'I think something was taken from that shop,' he said. 'I'm sure Clarence lost something he doesn't want to talk about – you do know about those rumours?'

'Someone wanting to blackmail him, you mean?' I asked. 'Had he got something there, I wonder, that would associate him with little boys?'

'It's a thought,' my colleague acknowledged. 'But what can we do? If he says nothing has been taken, how can we trace it?'

And so the mystery of the damage to Denby's Music Shop remained unsolved. Meanwhile, I had noticed a new development – Clarence was no longer attending his Masonic lodge in Eltering. For a time, this seemed of little or no significance because, so far as I knew, a Mason could resign his membership at any time.

I knew also that a Mason could be excluded from his lodge if there was sufficient cause, provided that a notice in writing was served upon him. That notice had to contain particulars of the complaint made against him. So had someone made a complaint against Clarence?

Other than to make a mental note of Clarence's changed circumstances, I did not pursue the matter; after all, it was not of any professional concern to me.

It would be some four months later when I called at his Eltering shop to buy some records. I wanted a selection of Chopin's music, in particular an album containing his Nocturne in E Flat, Opus 9, No. 2. I like all piano music, but this is one of my favourite pieces. Clarence was not in the shop that day and so Peggy, his voluble assistant, served me. I made my choice and said,

'Has he heard any more about his break-in?'

'Not a sausage, Mr Rhea. But then he wouldn't, would he?'

'Why not?' I was puzzled by her remark.

'It was the Freemasons,' she said. 'Everybody knows that. They want him out – he refuses to resign.'

'Why do they want him to resign?' I asked.

'Those rumours about him, little boys and that. You must have heard.'

'Yes, but there was nothing in them, was there?'

She shrugged her shoulders. 'The folks hereabouts all thought there was.'

'And you?' I pressed.

'I just work here,' she said. 'I've nothing against old Clarence, not personally, and I've seen nothing that would make me worry. But, well, you know what gossip is.'

'But the Masons wouldn't base their decisions on gossip, would they?'

'Maybe some of the Masons have little lads, Mr Rhea. Maybe they couldn't bear to think of him being one of them when the town was rich with rumours, bad though it might be.'

I thought fast. If the Masons had no proof of Clarence's

sexual misbehaviour, then they could not exclude him from
the lodge. They could not base such a decision on mere
speculation, and if he refused to resign, then they were
compelled to retain him, however embarrassing.

'So how does this break in link him and the Masons?' I
asked, now that she was so chatty.

'His regalia, Mr Rhea. He's not told anybody this, I know,
but he kept it upstairs, in a cupboard. When he went to the
lodge, he called here first to collect his little bag, then off he
went to the meeting. Whoever broke in took that bag, that's
all. No money, no records. Just his regalia.'

Now I could see what she was telling me. The rules of the
Freemasons say that no brother shall be admitted to a meeting
without the clothing appropriate to his rank. Without his
clothing, he could not be admitted, and unless he was
admitted, he could do nothing about the loss.

If what Peggy said was true, then poor old Clarence had
been denied admission to his Masonic meetings in a way that
barred him completely. But why? Because of rumour?
Because his conduct now lacked the necessary purity, or
because he had offended against the Freemason's concept of
moral law? Or had his loss been the action of a rogue
Freemason, someone acting without the knowledge of his
brothers? Or was it someone unconnected with the
Freemasons? Someone who knew how to inflict the maximum
embarrassment upon Clarence? I do not know – I could not
believe that the Brotherhood would stoop to this kind of
behaviour.

Clearly, I could not question Clarence on this delicate
matter – he was adamant that nothing had been stolen. Even
so, I did tend to believe Peggy's version of events.

Clarence continued to live in my beat and to run his
constantly successful music shop, but not once did I have
cause to suspect him of improper behaviour with children.
Then he died. It was a very sudden death: when driving to
work one day, he had a heart attack in his car, crashed through
some railings and ended that final journey on the banks of a

stream near Brantsford. His death revived all those memories of the veiled allegations against him, and even then, we had no proof that he had ever committed such low crimes. Clarence was buried in Elsinby churchyard and it was a big funeral, with his mother in attendance, for she was still alive.

I attended out of respect for him and watched his coffin being lowered into the earth.

That night, I was on duty from 10 p.m. until 6 a.m., and my patrol area included Eltering. At half past four in the morning, I was checking lock-up premises, one of which was Clarence's Music Shop. Peggy was running it until his will was executed – we all thought she would inherit it, which in fact she did.

As I reached into the dark recess of the doorway to turn the doorknob in my check on its security, I was aware of a parcel on the floor. I picked it up; it was wrapped in brown paper with no name on it, so I opened it, thinking it was an item of lost property.

But it contained a number of Masonic items and on one of the leather apron pouches inside the box was the name 'C'. Denby'.

Someone had returned Clarence's regalia.

10 The Feast of Christmas

Lay thy sheaf adown and come,
Share my harvest and my home.
Thomas Hood (1799–1845)

Christmas is a time for forgiving and for giving and in the country districts especially it is a period of true happiness and genuine friendliness. People visit one another, they help one another, they invite one another into their homes to share a drink or a meal and they give presents to people who have befriended them or helped them during the year. People such as the dustman, the milkman, the postman, the paper delivery lady and others are duly rewarded with suitable gifts, and we all go around with happy smiles on our faces.

Country policemen get Christmas gifts too. Some unwise souls regard these as attempted bribes, something to persuade the constable to turn a blind eye to minor breaches of the law, but in the mind of the rural dweller, there is no such evil intent. The present is given as a means of saying a sincere 'thank you', and if the constable persists in not accepting it, then the donor may be hurt or offended. Some givers will say it is not for the policeman, but for his wife and family, but whatever the circumstances of such a gift, it is never intended as a way of diverting the constable from doing his duty. City constables might have different views on such actions.

The truth is that country people know their constables as individuals and would never respect one who shirked his duty for whatever reason. Without their respect, he could not undertake his work. If the constable has to summons a countryman who has just given him a brace of pheasants, then that must be done without fear or favour. The pheasant-giver would not expect any favourable treatment, nor would he get it.

I became acutely aware of such matters about a week before Christmas when I called on a farmer called Dick Ferguson who lived at Thackerston. His well-tended farm was called Broom Hill and the house stood high above the village; the hillside below was covered with acres of broom, as it had been for centuries. It was a riot of brilliant golden yellow in the early summer.

Dick, a stockily built man in his early sixties, had long specialized in pig farming. He exhibited his best stock at local agricultural shows and was a frequent prize-winner, but he was a down-to-earth and highly practical man. I don't think Dick had an enemy in the world either. This might have been owing to his great honesty or even his generosity – at shows, he could be found in the bar, buying drinks for friends and competitors alike, while at home he was generous to the village hall, the WI, the church and all the local organizations. He always ensured they had enough prizes for their raffles or enough fresh food for their entertaining.

He'd even go down to the hall to help set up tables or sweep the floor if necessary. Nothing was too much trouble for Dick.

Just before that Christmas, I had to visit him to obtain a witness's statement. He'd been driving home from Harrogate when he'd witnessed a minor traffic accident in Knaresborough. Two cars had collided and a man had been injured. Typical of Dick, he'd stopped at the scene to help and had given his name to the injured man before the ambulance had carried him off. I had to interview Dick to establish exactly what he'd seen. It was a chill day in early December and I called at mid-morning.

'Come in, Mr Rhea. Sit thyself down and have a drink – it's very near Christmas,' were his opening words.

'A soft drink, thanks,' I said. 'I'm driving!'

'Sensible chap, thoo's as wise as a jinny owlet.' And his wife, Dorothy, produced two mugs of coffee, two buttered scones and a slice of gingerbread each with a slice of cheese to accompany it. Thus fortified, I settled down to the interview, first eliciting the story as Dick saw it. He was a good witness, giving me a clear account of precisely what had occurred, and I wrote down his words, getting him to sign his statement which would be sent to Knaresborough Police for whatever action they deemed necessary.

'Will I have to go to court?' he asked.

'It depends,' I said. 'If that man in the Ford Cortina is prosecuted for careless driving – and it does seem he was at fault – then you might have to give evidence. That's if he pleads not guilty. If he admits careless driving, I don't think they'll call you, but what you've just told me will help the Prosecution Department to decide whether or not to summons him.'

'So if I do have to go to court, I'll just tell 'em what I've told you, as straight as a bulrush?'

'Just that. Give them facts, not opinions,' I advised him, and then I explained a little of the procedure in a magistrates' court, detailing what would occur if a careless driving case was heard. He'd never been in court before and I felt he'd benefit from a little foreknowledge. I answered a few of his questions about the intricacies of giving evidence and warned him of the sort of cross-examination he might have to endure. He seemed to understand it all and thanked me for my guidance.

I remained a few more minutes chatting to Dick and Dorothy in their comfortable lounge about local matters, and he offered me a Christmas whisky, a lovely malt. Most reluctantly, I had to refuse – to drink whisky in uniform and then drive a police vehicle would be very stupid, but I did appreciate his gesture. I accepted a bitter lemon, however, a token of the proffered Christmas spirit, and wished them both seasonal greetings.

As I got up to leave, he said, 'Come wi' me, Mr Rhea.'

He led me into a huge beamed kitchen, and hanging from

the ceiling on strong metal hooks were dozens of cured hams. At that time, some people, like Dick, still did their own pig-killing and ham-curing, using methods handed down from generation to generation. A strong home-cured Yorkshire ham was one of life's great treats and the farmers in this region would slice off pieces as they required them and cook them for breakfast. I'd been brought up to similar practices, surviving the Second World War with the fruits of the countryside – pheasants, grouse, salmon, home-cured ham, home-grown potatoes, soft fruit and apples, home-produced milk, cream and cheese, brambles and wild mushrooms – it all formed part of the luxury of rustic living. Broom Hill, thanks to Dick and Dorothy, was perpetuating that highly desirable style of life.

'Somebody's been busy,' was all I could think of saying as I gazed on this forest of suspended hams.

'Heat from working kitchens is good for 'em,' he said. 'They allus used to hang hams in t'kitchen rafters. You have to know t'right method, right time to salt them, and then t'right amount of salt, saltpetre, vinegar and a spot o' sugar – then hang 'em up like this, where there's a bit of smoke from t'kitchen fire, not so as they get too dry mind or too hot.... If they get too dry and hot, t'skin gets as tough as bog oak ... '

He stood on a chair and lifted one of them down, passing it to me. I took it in my outstretched arms and almost dropped it – it was so heavy, like a huge, weighty stone.

But I held on to it. I could smell the strength of that ham; I could imagine it sizzling with roast potatoes ... it was mouth-watering.

'This is what a ham should be like,' I complimented him. 'I'll bet it tastes smashing ... '

'It's yours,' he said. 'Take it. For Christmas, for t'missus and your bairns.'

'No,' I protested weakly. 'I can't, not all this!'

'Well a few slices isn't any good to anybody,' he said. 'It's yours, take it.'

'How much?' I asked.

'How much he asks ... nowt, dammit man. It's Christmas,

you've been good to me, explaining about that court business, so it's me saying thanks to you, Mr Rhea. Nowt no less, nowt no more.'

I persisted with my weak refusals, but succumbed. A ham this size would last us months. I bore it home in triumph and Mary was overwhelmed – like me, she was born and bred in the Yorkshire countryside and knew the wholesome value of a home-cured ham. There was a hook in the pantry and I hung it there to await the time we cut the first slice.

About a week later, there was a knock on the door and when I opened it, Dick was standing there, carrying another equally huge ham on his shoulder. For the briefest of moments, I thought he'd forgotten about giving me the first one, and that this was another ...

'Come in,' I said.

He stomped in and I helped him to lift the enormous ham from his powerful shoulder, still wondering why he had come.

'You've still got that ham I gave you, have you?' he asked in his blunt Yorkshire way.

'Yes, untouched, Dick. We're saving it for a special occasion.

'Aye, well, good. Well, I hope you don't mind me coming like this, but I'd like it back – and this 'un's yours, not that first 'un.'

I was puzzled for a moment, and said, 'But they look the same to me.'

'Aye, well, they're not. That first 'un's for t'Brewers Arms, so I'll leave this new leg and if you give me t'old 'un back, then we'll say no more about it.'

I took the new one and went to the pantry where I lifted down the original, then as I handed it to him, I asked,

'Dick, just what is the difference, if you don't mind me asking? I can't see anything different.... '

'Salt, Mr Rhea. That 'un for t'pub, 'as got a lot more salt on it. Salt's good for beer sales, you see, Mr Rhea. When t'regulars eat sandwiches made from that ham, they'll guzzle gallons o' beer afterwards. It's an arrangement I have with

George – I allus gives 'is hams an extra dollop or two of strong salt. They're as salty as Lot's wife.'

'So it's a good job we didn't eat it!' I laughed.

'Aye, you'd have been as dry as our vicar's sermons!' he chortled.

Having accepted the swop, I asked, 'How about you then, Dick? You'll be a bit dry after lugging that ham up here?'

'Just a bit,' he said.

'I've got a nice malt whisky,' I said. 'How about having a Christmas drink with me?'

'If I get as tipsy as a fiddler's bitch, I can allus walk home,' he said, following me into the lounge.

* * *

Dick's generosity was in direct contrast to the attitude of old Mr Morley. Well into his seventies, he lived alone in a neat but somewhat isolated brick-built bungalow beside the road leading from Thackerston to Ploatby, and few of the villagers, if any, knew his Christian name. Everybody called him Mr Morley – when his wife was alive, she had always referred to him as Mr Morley, and never as 'my husband' or 'our Fred', or whatever his name was.

Because of the loneliness of his bungalow, I would pop in when I was passing, especially if the weather was wintry, because his route to the shops was easily cut-off by snow. I would ask if he needed anything from the shops and, from time to time, he would ask me to bring something back, such as a tin of baked beans or packet of corn flakes. I know the other callers did likewise. His only mode of travel was an old black bike which he'd had for years, but he rarely left his home – he had no need to. When he did emerge, he always wore a black beret. The sight of the little man in the black beret, aboard an old black bike, was a familiar one in those lanes, especially in the summer months. I think he sold some of his flowers in the local shops.

His neighbours, distant though they were, were kind to

him, doing his errands, shopping for his clothes, giving him food and sometimes taking him hot meals. A nearby farmer's wife always cooked his Sunday lunch, for example, and took it to him on a tray, a journey of about a mile and a half.

Mr Morley did have relatives, but they lived in the Midlands and, in any case, were not very close to him. He had no sons or daughters, those relations being distant cousins so far as I could establish. He had never been to visit them, and, so far as anyone knew, they had never come to see him. His only link with most of them was the occasional Christmas card, but one of them, the daughter of one of his distant cousins, did send him a Christmas cake every year.

For all the kindness displayed by his neighbours, old Mr Morley never returned their generosity, not even asking them to sit down for a cup of tea or to share a Christmas drink. I don't think he was mean or distrusting; I think he simply did not think about inviting any one to share a few quiet moments with him.

On the few occasions I had been inside his house, I had found it clean, tidy and well decorated. Some elderly men, living alone, tend to ignore the appearance of their paintwork and wallpaper, but to give Mr Morley his due credit, he did keep a nice home. His garden was also neat and tidy, for he spent a lot of time among his flowers and vegetables, but never gave any to his callers.

Conversely, they did not expect anything for their generosity, but sometimes I felt that the farmer's wife who brought his Sunday lunch would have enjoyed the occasional gift of a bunch of his lovely flowers, and some of the ladies who did his shopping would have welcomed a bag of carrots or sprouts.

But those thoughts were not important; the important thing was to make sure he was cared for, and in that we all took our turn, albeit without any requests either from Mr Morley or anyone else. He was alone and so the villagers looked after him.

Then, one day, just before Christmas, I received a

privileged insight into his character. It was a bitterly cold day as I halted my van outside his garden gate. I was passing and thought I'd pop in to ask whether he needed anything, but as I walked up the path to his back door, I saw that it was standing open. I rapped and called out, 'Anyone around? Are you there, Mr Morley? Hello?'

He was not in the kitchen and so I checked his garden and outbuildings before going into the bungalow, but there was no sign of him. I returned to the kitchen door and repeated my knocking and shouting, and then I thought I heard a soft cry.

I was slightly alarmed. I called his name and went into the house, announcing my own name as I progressed to minimize any alarm he might experience. I found him in his living room, slumped in an armchair, and he seemed to be dazed.

'Mr Morley?' I called to him, and he responded, his grey eyes blinking at me. 'What's happened?'

'Oh, hello, Mr Rhea. Glad you've come … it was a dizzy spell … just came over me … '

'I'll get the doctor to look at you,' I said.

'He's been. I've some tablets.' He pointed to the kitchen. 'Above the sink, in a brown bottle, heart … it's my age, you know.'

'And you've not taken one this morning like you should have done, is that it?'

'Aye,' he said.

I went into the kitchen for the required tablet and a glass of water, but couldn't find the brown bottle. I looked in various other cupboards – and found a miser's hoard! One cupboard, clean and neatly arranged, was full of Christmas cakes, all looking very much alike. I counted a dozen – twelve Christmas cakes all sitting there. And in another, there were bottles of spirits – whisky, gin, brandy – all unopened. I counted six bottles of whisky alone, and then in another cupboard, there were boxes of chocolates, dozens of them, all neatly stacked in piles.

Then I found the tablets, read the instructions and tipped one into the palm of my hand. I ran a glass of water and took the treatment to him. He swallowed the tablet with a grunt and thanked me.

'I'll get the doctor to pop in,' I said. 'Now, your fire's not lit, and it's cold outside, so I'll light it while I'm here.'

'Mrs Pennock'll do it when she brings my dinner,' he said. 'It's Wednesday, you see.'

'I'll do it, Mr Morley. It'll save her a job.'

And so I buckled down to the task of cleaning out his grate and lighting the fire, finding that he did have a stock of chopped kindling in an outside shed, and a large stock of coal. So he was not a miser in the sense that he did not want to spend money, so I wondered about his massive stocks of cakes, chocolates and booze.

As I worked on lighting the fire, I chattered to him, asking what he would be doing this Christmas and whether he'd be seeing any of his relatives. He said he'd be at home like he always was, but that Mrs Bowes had invited him to share Christmas dinner with her and her husband. He'd accepted.

'I see you're all right for Christmas cakes,' I said, my curiosity getting the better of me. Why did he keep so many?

'It's our Alice's lass,' he said. 'She sends one every year.'

'But you don't eat them?' I smiled.

'No, I'm allergic to dried fruit – it brings me out in spots, so I can't eat fruit cake, Mr Rhea.'

'You ought to tell her!' I suggested, sweeping up the dust from his hearth. 'You've enough cakes to feed the whole of this dale!'

'They keep well,' he said.

'They're for eating, not for keeping,' I chided him. 'You could send some into York, for the poor folks there. There's loads of charitable organizations would welcome them, Mr Morley, and you'd know they'd gone to a useful place. Are you allergic to whisky as well?'

'Aye, I can't drink spirits, you see, so when folks give me bottles, I never drink 'em. I don't mind a bottle of beer now and then, but not spirits.'

'And chocolates?'

'Allergic to chocolate an' all, so I keep them … '

By that time I had finished the fireplace and ensured that a good roaring fire was warming the room, the pill had achieved its purpose and he had recovered from his dizzy spell. I told him where the bottle was and warned him to make sure he took his pills on time in accordance with the doctor's instructions. He promised he would, but, being an old man, I felt concerned that he might forget from time to time. But I was reassured by the number of people who called in – like me, one of them would probably find him if he needed help.

After getting the fire going, I asked if he'd like a cup of tea or coffee, and he smiled. 'Aye, I would,' he said. I had to ask him – he'd never think of asking me! I made two mugs of coffee and sat with him for about an hour; we talked about Christmas time, about it being a time for giving, about the events that had been arranged in the surrounding villages like the old folks' parties, the church events, the children's parties, whist drives and so on.

'You know, Mr Morley,' I said, 'those parties and events would welcome anything you don't need for raffle prizes – like those bottles of gin or whisky and some of those boxes of chocolates, and Christmas cakes for sharing with the old folks.'

'Aye, but them's all presents to me.' He shook his grey head. 'You can't go about giving presents away, can you?'

'What happened to the earlier cakes, then?' I asked.

'My missus used to give 'em away. Them in my kitchen's come since our Elsie passed on, Mr Rhea – she'd have handed 'em out to somebody … '

'But you could do the same! If Mrs Morley did it, then so can you. You could always give people like Mrs Pennock a box of chocolates, as a thanks for bringing your dinners in.'

'Aye, well, I'll think about it.'

I left him, now confident that he would survive, but I did tell both the doctor and the district nurse about Mr Morley and they said they'd make regular calls.

But the next time I called was after that Christmas. There

had been a heavy fall of snow overnight and I popped in to ask if he was all right. He was – his fire was blazing, someone had brought in some logs and I could see the remains of a hefty meal on the table.

'I was just passing, Mr Morley, and thought I'd check to see if you're all right.'

'Very well, thanks, Mr Rhea. I had a nice Christmas.'

'Did you get any nice presents,' I asked.

'Aye, three bottles of whisky, two bottles of gin, a lovely cake from our Alice's lass and some chocolates from the neighbours.'

'And what have you done with them?' I asked him.

'They're in the cupboards,' he said. 'With the others.'

And so they were. He had not given any of his earlier gifts away, and so his stock had now increased. And it increased every year. I did try to persuade him that he should give generously to local charitable organizations but, for some reason, he would never part with any of his presents, however unwanted they were. And not once did he give anything to any of his helpers – I realized that my solitary cup of coffee with him was indeed an unusual event.

But then I realized I'd had to ask him for it.

So suppose people asked him for a donation to their function? Would he then give generously?

Some weeks later, the Reverend Simon Hamilton, vicar of St Andrew's parish church in Elsinby, mentioned that he was arranging a spring fête to raise money for repairs to the tower. He would be staging a tombola and there would be teas, as well as the usual attractions.

'Do you ever pop in to visit old Mr Morley?' I asked him.

'Regularly,' he said. 'At least once a week.'

I mentioned my own visits and we shared experiences, and then I said, 'Look, vicar, if you need bottles of spirits, Christmas cakes or boxes of chocolates, he's got dozens stacked away. He never uses any of them – they're all unwanted gifts. If you were to ask if he had something for your fête, he might decide to part with one of his treasures! But you'd have to ask, he'll never volunteer a gift!'

'I'll try it!' he beamed.

A week before the fête, I saw the vicar in Elsinby and we discussed parking arrangements and other professional matters, then I asked.

'Old Mr Morley, did you ask him for something for your fête?'

'I did,' he smiled.

'And?' I asked.

'Nothing,' he laughed. 'He said he hadn't anything to give away.'

★   ★   ★

Another fascinating character was Miss Gertrude Midgley who lived in the end cottage of a row of cute terraced houses in Maddleskirk. The row comprises six tiny stone-built homes, each with only one bedroom, a bathroom/toilet, a kitchen and a lounge. There were no garages, although each house had a tiny yard and a patch of hillside garden behind. The front doors opened onto the village street and each of the cottages was occupied by a solitary elderly lady. Six old ladies therefore occupied the entire block known as Field Houses, with Gertrude in No. 6.

She had worked in service during her youth, being employed in several country houses in Ryedale, first as a servant girl and later as a housekeeper. Her latter years had been spent as the dinner lady in the primary school in Maddleskirk, from where she had retired some twenty years earlier. Many of the villagers remembered her time at the school – she was a strict, no-nonsense lady who could keep the children in order during their dinner break. Now about eighty years old, she was spritely for her age and managed to do all her own shopping by using the local buses or pottering down to the village shops.

She was a plump person, perhaps typical of ladies who cared for the appetites of country gentlemen and their friends, and, latterly, schoolchildren. She wore her grey hair in a neat bun, tied with a coloured ribbon. Her face was round and she had ruddy cheeks, but she lacked the perpetual smile of so many cooking ladies.

In some respects, she was a grey figure – she always wore long grey dresses which came to below her knees, and seemed to perpetually wear sandals over her thick grey lisle stockings. She wore greyish cardigans, too, and seldom seemed to enjoy bright colours upon her, except for that ribbon in her hair – it would be red one day, blue another, then yellow, green or even purple or white.

So far as anyone knew, there had never been a romance in her life and she did not appear to have any family who might visit her or whom she might call on. I know she did visit people in the village, and they called on her, either to check that she was all right or to have a cup of tea or a natter with her. But it never occurred to me that I should call. After all, she was hale and hearty, she had a stream of callers and was not the sort of person who would come to the notice of the police or the social services for any reason.

It was with some surprise, therefore, that I saw her waving to me from her front door some two weeks before Christmas. I was walking along the village street on one of my foot patrols when she hailed me.

'Mr Rhea,' she beckoned. 'Can you spare a minute?'

'Of course,' and so I followed her into her cottage. A fire was blazing in the black-leaded grate and an old-fashioned kettle, large and black, was singing on the hob. A rocking chair stood at one side of the fireplace, and a comfortable old easy chair was at the other.

A clip mat lay before the fire, while the mantelpiece was full of brassware – lots of candlesticks large and small, vases, animal figures and so on. It looked very cosy.

'Sit down.' She pointed to the easy chair. 'You'll have a cup of tea?'

As it was more of a command than an invitation, I obeyed and indicated that I'd love one. She disappeared into the kitchen and returned with a plate of scones which she placed on the hearth, followed by two mugs, a bowl of sugar and jug of milk. She poured the hot water into the tea pot and sat down in the rocking chair, allowing it to move as she settled down.

'You never came last year,' she said. 'So I thought I'd better remind you this time.'

I was puzzled by her comment. 'Last year?' I shook my head. 'I'm not sure what you mean, Miss Midgley.'

'The policeman always calls to cut my cake,' she said.

'Your Christmas cake, you mean?' I guessed that was the subject of her remarks.

'Aye, what else?'

'I'm sorry,' I tried to express my feelings by the movements of my hands, 'but I had no idea. I mean, if I had known, I'd have called especially.'

'Well, make sure you call this year then – Christmas Day or Boxing Day, not before. And before New Year. Make sure you get it cut before New Year.'

As I pondered over my newly imposed duties, she poured the tea and handed me one of the mugs and the sugar.

'No sugar, thanks,' I smiled, but accepted one of the scones. 'So who did cut your cake last year?' I ventured.

'Nobody, so it's still in my pantry. You'll cut it before you leave, I should think.'

'Yes, of course.' The scone was delicious, home-made with lots of rich butter oozing into it. 'I'll be delighted.'

She produced the delicious-looking cake which stood on a large wooden board; it would be about eight inches square by two inches deep, but lacked any icing. A knife lay beside it. She placed the board on the table in her lounge and I went across, wondering if there was any ceremonial method of performing this task, or speech to be made, but there did not seem to be any formalities. I simply slid the knife into the cake in the centre and sliced it through.

'Cut yourself a slice,' she said. 'And me.'

I chopped two slices and we returned to the fireside where I tasted the cake. It was delicious, moist and very highly flavoured with brandy or malt whisky so far as I could tell. That had preserved it well.

'Happy Christmas for last year,' I said.

'And you,' she returned.

As I chomped the year-old piece of cake, I wondered what all this was about, and decided to ask. I guessed she would never enlighten me unless I did ask.

'Why does the policeman have to cut your Christmas cake?' I ventured.

'It's my custom.' She actually smiled this time. 'My grandad was a policeman. He rose to be sergeant,' she added with pride. 'I had no brothers or sisters, and Dad died early – he was a railwayman. But I allus say, if I'd been a lad, I'd have joined the force. Girls didn't do that in my day, Mr Rhea, you see. Anyroad, Grandad allus cut our cake for Christmas, and when he passed on, I got other policemen to do the job. Last year was the first time I'd missed … '

'I'm sorry, I had no idea, otherwise I would have called in.'

'I'm not grumbling,' she said. 'There's no point in grumbling about things, but I've got it done now, and I know you'll call this year come Christmas.'

'I will, I promise,' I assured her.

I remained a few more minutes and learned that she would spend her Christmas alone. She had no relations, and had no wish to inflict herself upon any other family who did have friends or relations to visit them. I made a determined vow to visit her on Christmas Day – at least she'd have a visitor on that very special day.

'You could always come to us,' I heard myself saying. 'We always have a crowd in – my wife and I are both from big families.'

'No, Mr Rhea, I know what family life is like at Christmas and I will not intrude, but thanks for the thought.'

'You could pop down to one of the hotels, perhaps? Or contact one of the charities who arrange dinner for lots of people like yourself … '

'I'll have no charity, Mr Rhea!' she was firm. 'I'm fit and

healthy, and I can cook myself a nice Christmas dinner without relying on other folks. No, you forget me, leave me alone and I'll manage. It's my lot in life to be alone, without a husband or kids, and I'll not grumble about it. So just you mind on and come to cut my cake, that's all I ask.'

I tried to persuade her to allow me to make an approach on her behalf, to ask around to see if there were any gatherings to which she might be invited for Christmas Day, but she steadfastly refused. In some ways, I had to admire her sturdy determination, but I did feel she must be a very lonely old lady.

I left with a slab of her Christmas cake in my pocket for Mary and the children, and continued my patrol of Maddleskirk before heading for home in Aidensfield. In the days that followed, I did learn that she always spent Christmas alone and that others in the village had invited her to join them – her neighbours in Field Houses, for example, had extended lots of invitations. She did visit them at other times, but because each had their family in at Christmas, or went to their family, Miss Midgley refused to be a 'nuisance' as she put it.

It would be about a week after my visit that I found myself embroiled in the preparations for the Eltering Sub-Divisional Police Children's Christmas Party. It was to be held in the Whistler Hall at Eltering and all children of police officers in Eltering Sub-Division were invited. It would be held on the Wednesday between Christmas and New Year from 3 p.m. until 7 p.m. The mums would share the chore of making cakes and jellies, dads would decorate the hall and organize games, and the parents had arranged some music and entertainment, my part being that of the magician. I hoped my famous Chinese Rings would survive the assault of many hands as the kids tried to separate them after I had magically joined them. Sergeant Bairstow was to be Father Christmas and all the children would receive a present.

Mrs Bairstow was in charge of the feeding arrangements, co-ordinating the work of all the other ladies, and it was always a very happy, if very tiring, occasion. Then, two days before the party, Mrs Bairstow's mother was taken ill – Mrs Bairstow had to rush off to care for her. Sergeant Bairstow was not needed at her side and so remained to fulfil both his police and Yuletide duties.

'We could do with another pair of hands,' he said to me. 'My missus did a good job at that party, you need somebody to organize things....'

It was then that I thought of Miss Midgley.

'I think I know somebody,' I told him, and explained about Gertrude and her association with policemen.

'Isn't she a bit old?' That was his only reservation.

I shook my head. 'She'll be tired afterwards, we will all be,' I said. 'But I'll bet she'll be happy.'

'OK, Nick, ask her. We can fetch and carry her.'

When I went on Christmas Day to cut her Christmas cake for the current year, therefore, I took her a small present from Mary, me and the children, and then put the proposal to her.

'Nay, Mr Rhea, I'm too old for that sort of thing – I've lost my touch now.'

But I could sense the wistfulness in her voice and began to convince her that she could do the job. I reminded her of her days organizing school dinners, her work in the country houses, her knowledge of food, her ability to get along with others ... In time, she weakened.

'Well, if you honestly think I could do it,' she said.

'I do, otherwise I wouldn't be here, asking!' I said.

She hesitated and then nodded. 'I'll do it,' she smiled.

'Right, I'll pick you up at one o'clock,' I said, and then explained the overall arrangements. When I called for her, she had changed into another frock, a pretty pink and blue one, and I saw she'd had her hair done too. This was clearly a very important outing. Her reserve was broken when one of the mums recognized her as her own dinner lady at school, and from that point, Gertrude entered the spirit of our party.

She organized the plates for the children, making sure none got two plates and that they all got a jelly and a beaker of orange squash. Her no-nonsense manner endeared her to the other women for she was a natural organizer, being able to spot the need for extra food long before it arose, keeping the children in order and ensuring that they all cleared away their own plates – just like they did at school. Afterwards, when Father Christmas distributed the presents, there was one for Gertrude, from all the children. I could see she was truly moved.

As I drove her home, I asked, 'Well, did you enjoy that?'

'Mr Rhea, it was lovely, the best Christmas I've had for, well, I daren't say. I really did enjoy myself – and I know my grandad would have been pleased to see me there. And a present as well. It was really lovely, a marvellous day.'

'We were all pleased to see you there,' I said, for it was true. She had been marvellous. 'So how about next year?'

'If they'll have me,' she said.

'They will,' I assured her. I let her out of the car and helped her up the steps into her cottage.

'Happy Christmas, Miss Midgley,' I said, holding open her cottage door.

'And you – and don't forget to come next year!' she reminded me, disappearing inside. 'I'll have another cake waiting.'